Exploring maths

Class Book

Anita Straker, Tony Fisher, Rosalyn Hyde, Sue Jennings and Jonathan Longstaffe

PEARSON
Longman

2

Published and distributed by Pearson Education Limited, Edinburgh Gate, Harlow, Essex, CM20 2JE, England

www.longman.co.uk

First published 2008
Second impression 2008

ISBN-13 978-1-405-84408-6

Freelance development editor: Sue Glover

Typeset by Tech-Set, Gateshead

Printed and bound in China SWTC/02

The publisher's policy is to use paper manufactured from sustainable forests.

Picture Credits
The publisher would like to thank the following for their kind permission to reproduce their photographs:
(Key: b-bottom; c-centre; l-left; r-right; t-top)

Alamy Images: Alvey & Towers Picture Library 211; Jon Arnold Images Ltd 302; Philip Brittan 1tl, 51c; Bubbles Photolibrary 183t; Scott Camazine 281c; Greg Balfour Evans 271; Robert Fried 234tr; GoGo Images Corporation 184t; Jeff Greenberg 306c; Sally and Richard Greenhill 319c; David Gregs 89; Andrew Holt 182l, 295; Chris Howes/Wild Places Photography 226; Maurice Joseph 214; JUPITERIMAGES/ Brand X 101t; JUPITERIMAGES/ Thinkstock 64; Justin Leighton 14, 180; Mediablitzimages (uk) Limited 42c; Jeff Morgan education 281t; Gianni Muratore 310t; Oramstock 109b; Photofusion Picture Library 69b, 134; David Robertson 292l; Mark Scheuern 272; Alex Segre 279; Branislav Senic 187; Tetra Images 167r; The London Art Archive 282b; The Photolibrary Wales 95, 188; Martin Usborne 346; Rob Walls 306r; Ken Welsh 162b; Janine Wiedel Photolibrary 59, 311; **Ancient Art & Architecture:** John P.Stevens 234tl; **Bridgeman Art Library Ltd:** State Central Artillery Museum, St. Petersburg, Russia 147; **Corbis:** Bettmann 29, 54; Jonathan Blair 182r; Tim De Waele 70b; Najlah Feanny 76; Michael Freeman 189; Alan Schein Photography 225; Ariel Skelley 7; Paul A. Souders 30; Roger Wood 65; **Danita Delimont. com:** Nik Wheeler 162t; **DK Images:** 49r, 62r, 137, 222, 234b, 236, 249r, 250, 269r, 289 (1st row (3)), 289 (3rd row (1)), 289 (5th row (2)); Ian Aitken © Rough Guides 183b; Paul Bricknell 108c, 110l, 110r, 176b, 210b; The British Museum 243; Courtesy of the Goodwood Festival of Speed 289 (6th row (2)); Andy Crawford 1b, 289 (4th row (2)), 289 (5th row (1)); Geoff Dann, The Wallace Collection, London 116c; Peter Gardner 276; Philip Gatward 212, 289 (2nd row (1)), 289 (2nd row (3)), 289 (3rd row (3)), 289 (5th row (3)), 289 (6th row (1)); Robin Gauldie 128; Steve Gorton 27, 49l, 70t, 99tc, 108l, 261, 319r, 329; Dave King 35, 97, 173t, 220l, 289 (1st row (2)), 289 (3rd row (2)), 289 (4th row (1)); Dave King/Courtesy of the University Museum of Archaeology and Anthropology, Cambridge 36, 112; Bob Langrish 167l; Judith Miller/ Dorling Kindersley/Branksome Antiques 116l; Judith Miller/Dorling Kindersley/Branksome Antiques 116tr; Ian O'Leary 51l, 190t; Stephen Oliver 220r, 229r, 233, 242; Roger Phillips 9; Rob Reichenfeld 347c; Dave Rudkin 289 (4th row (3)); David Murray and Jules Selmes 235; Steve Shott 1tr, 51r; Simon Smith 316; Clive Streeter 224; Matthew Ward 249l; Matthew Ward/Courtesy of Tallahassee Car Museum 289 (2nd row (2)); Andrew Whittuck 320t; Philip Wilkins 223; Jerry Young 192; **Mary Evans Picture Library:** GROSVENOR PRINTS 213; **Getty Images:** AFP 319l; Amwell/Stone 227l; Doug Armand/Stone 42t, 239c; Daniel Bosler/Stone 227; Jeffrey Coolidge/Iconica 281c; Laurence Dutton/The Image Bank 184b; Antony Edwards/The Image Bank 323br; Jon Eisberg/Taxi 244; Sean Ellis/Stone 99tl; Chris Everard/Stone 1tc; FPG/Taxi 99b; Derek P. Redfearn/The Image Bank 298t; Darren Robb/Stone 298b, 323bc; Micheal Simpson/Taxi 108r; Hugh Sitton/Stone 39; Jeff Spielman/The Image Bank 99tr, 245; Jess Stock/Stone 8; Keren Su/Taxi 306l; Alan Thornton/Stone 125b; Time & Life Pictures 267; **iStockphoto:** 190c, 209l, 210t, 289 (1st row (1)), 323t; Stefan Ataman 323bl; Galina Barskaya 68; Anthony Brown 129; Daniel Brunner 274b; Jared Cassidy 314; Greg Cooper 132; Jorge Delgado 231; Andrew Dernie 277; Gabriel Eckert 268t; Terrance Emerson 159tc; Sergey Galushko 173b; Bruce Gates 107t; Shawn Gearhart 31; Steve Geer 348t; Joe Gough 270; Clayton Hansen 347r; Jaap Hart 159tr; Loretta Hostettler 193; Gabor Izso 157l; Frank Richard Kebschull 157r; Steven Lewarne 241bl; Michael Madsen 21t; Steven Miric 107b; Pamela Moore 320b; Sandra O'Claire 28; Dori O'Connell 268b; Per Øyvind 190b; Edyta Pawłowska 205b; Joanna Pecha 343; Shawn Pecor 227c; Thomas Perkins 205t; Sergej Petrakov 101b; Toon Possemiers 140; Amanda Rohde 136b; Chris Schmidt 282t; Jean Schweitzer 249c; Alina Solovyova-Vincent 274t; James Troi 159tl; Joseph White 347l; Natthawat Wongrat 178t; Lisa F. Young 136t; **Jupiter Unlimited:** AbleStock.com 209r; Comstock Images 106, 125t; Liquidlibrary 58, 145; Photos. com 21b, 62c, 100, 159b, 172; Thinkstock Images 209c, 239l; **Kobal Collection Ltd:** DIMENSION FILMS 78b; **Jonathan Longstaffe:** 160, 348b, 348c; **MB Artists/John Manders:** 143, 280; **Nature Picture Library:** 182c; Niall Benvie 240; David Noton 241t; **Pearson Education Ltd:** 5, 42b, 73, 78t, 131, 135, 269l; EMG Education Management Group 46, 301; C. Marvin Lang 203; Pearson Learning Group 176t; Pearson Learning Photo Studio 169, 199, 289 (6th row (3)); PH College 167c, 177; Prentice Hall School Division 109t, 223c, 253, 275; Silver Burdett Ginn 48, 130, 220c, 223r, 229c, 229l, 299, 310b, 314; **Photolibrary.com:** 6, 168, 178b; Johner 37; **PunchStock:** Digital Vision 62l; Stockbyte 239r; **Frank Siteman:** 152; **Anita Straker:** 149, 313; **TopFoto:** Alistair Fuller 241brr

Cover images: Front: **Alamy Images:** Steven Haggard

All other images © Pearson Education

Picture Research by: Louise Edgeworth

Every effort has been made to trace the copyright holders and we apologise in advance for any unintentional omissions. We would be pleased to insert the appropriate acknowledgement in any subsequent edition of this publication.

Contents

Properties of numbers

This unit will help you to:

◉ work out square numbers;

◉ spot multiples of one-digit numbers;

◉ test numbers to see if they divide exactly by 2, 3, 4, 5 or 10;

◉ put positive and negative numbers in order;

◉ work out temperature differences.

1 Square numbers

This lesson will help you to work out square numbers.

Exercise 1

These objects are arranged in rectangular patterns.

3 × 4

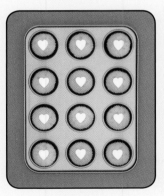

6 × 4

2 × 3

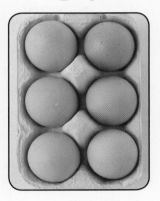

8 × 8

Square numbers can be arranged in *square* patterns.

64 is a square number because it can be arranged in 8 rows of 8.

A chess board has 8 × 8 = 64 small squares.

1 = 1 × 1 is the first square number.

4 = 2 × 2 is the second square number.

9 = 3 × 3 is the third square number.

16 = 4 × 4 is the fourth square number.

The first ten square numbers are:

$$1 \quad 4 \quad 9 \quad 16 \quad 25 \quad 36 \quad 49 \quad 64 \quad 81 \quad 100$$

There is a short way to write square numbers.
The fourth square number is 4^2. This means $4 \times 4 = 16$.
The tenth square number is 10^2. This means $10 \times 10 = 100$.

Use **multiplication** to work out bigger square numbers.

Example 1   Find the 14th square number.

Work out 14×14, which is 196.

You can **use your calculator** to work out square numbers.

Example 2   Find the 26th square number.

To find the 26th square number, press these keys: 2 6 x^2.

The display will show: 675

1   The second square number is $2 \times 2 = 4$. Work out:
   a   the 10th square number   b   the 15th square number
   c   the 20th square number   d   the 35th square number.

2   Copy and complete these square numbers.
   a $... \times ... = 64$ b $... \times ... = 81$ c $... \times ... = 121$
   d $... \times ... = 144$ e $... \times ... = 196$ f $... \times ... = 484$

3   Work out:
   a   half of the 10th square number
   b   twice the 6th square number
   c   double the 7th square number
   d   five times the 3rd square number
   e   the sum of the 3rd square number and the 5th square number
   f   the difference between the 5th square number and the 2nd square number
   g   the 6th square number divided by the 3rd square number
   h   the 2nd square number multiplied by the 5th square number.

4 The square numbers are:

1   4   9   16   25   36   49   64   81   100   121   144   ...

Write each of these numbers as the sum of two square numbers.
The numbers can be the same square numbers or different square numbers.
You can **use your calculator** if you wish.

a	25	b	50	c	17	d	29
e	85	f	52	g	61	h	125

Write each of these numbers as the difference of two square numbers.

i	3	j	16	k	20	l	15
m	36	n	21	o	64	p	77

 5 Copy and complete this pattern.

$$1 = 1^2$$
$$1 + 3 = 2^2$$
$$1 + 3 + 5 = \square^2$$
$$1 + 3 + 5 + 7 = \square^2$$
$$\square + \square + \square + \square + \square = \square^2$$

What is the answer to $1 + 3 + 5 + 7 + 9 + 11 + 13 + 15 + 17 + 19$?

Extension problem

 6 Any whole number can be written as the sum of four square numbers. For example:

$$23 = 1 + 4 + 9 + 9$$

Investigate different ways of writing 150 as the sum of four square numbers.
Use your calculator to help you.

🔘 **Points to remember**

- ⊙ A number multiplied by itself is a **square number**.
- ⊙ A square number can be shown as dots arranged in a square.
- ⊙ 81 is the square of 9. It can be written as 9^2.

2 Multiples and divisibility

This lesson will help you to spot multiples and test numbers to see if they divide exactly by 2, 3, 4, 5 or 10.

Exercise 2

A **multiple** of a number divides exactly by the number.

Here are some of the multiples of 3:

$3 \times 1 = 3$

$3 \times 2 = 6$

$3 \times 3 = 9$

$3 \times 4 = 12$

Numbers in the 3 times table are multiples of 3.

1	2	3	4	5	6	7	8	9	10
11	12	13	14	15	16	17	18	19	20
21	22	23	24	25	26	27	28	29	30
31	32	33	34	35	36	37	38	39	40
41	42	43	44	45	46	47	48	49	50
51	52	53	54	55	56	57	58	59	60
61	62	63	64	65	66	67	68	69	70
71	72	73	74	75	76	77	78	79	80
81	82	83	84	85	86	87	88	89	90
91	92	93	94	95	96	97	98	99	100

Multiples of 2 are **even numbers**.
Even numbers end in 2, 4, 6, 8 or 0.

Whole numbers that are not even are **odd numbers**.
Any number that ends in 1, 3, 5, 7 or 9 is odd.

A **test** for a multiple of 3 is to see if a number divides exactly by 3.
60 is a multiple of 3 because $60 \div 3 = 20$ with no remainder.

You can also test if a number is a multiple like this. A number is:

    divisible by **2** if its last digit is 0, 2, 4, 6 or 8;

    divisible by **3** if the sum of its digits is divisible by 3;

    divisible by **4** if half of it is even, or if its last two digits are divisible by 4;

    divisible by **5** if its last digit is 5 or 0;

    divisible by **10** if its last digit is 0.

Example

Is 78 divisible by 3?

Method 1

The whole-number answer of 26 tells you that 78 is divisible by 3.

Method 2

The digit sum of 78 is $7 + 8 = 15$.
15 is a multiple of 3 because it is in the 3 times table.
So 78 is a multiple of 3.

1   Write down the first three multiples of each of these numbers.

    a 10   b 3   c 6   d 9   e 21

2   Write **True** or **False**.

    a 12 is a multiple of 2.   b 14 is divisible by 7.

    c 26 is a multiple of 3.   d 72 is a multiple of 9.

    e 9 is a multiple of 27.   f 6 is a multiple of 1.

    g 105 is divisible by 5 and by 2.   h 36 is divisible by 4 and by 9.

3   Which of these are multiples of 9?

       18   32   56   64   72

4   Three of these numbers are multiples of 3 **and** multiples of 5. Which numbers are they?

       35   45   36   40   25   30   60

5   **Use your calculator** to check these.

    a Is 142 divisible by 7?

    b Is 266 divisible by 7?

    c Is 402 divisible by 8?

    d Is 144 divisible by 8?

    e Is 324 divisible by 9?

    f Is 127 divisible by 9?

6   Here are four digit cards.

       3   5   4   6

    Use each of the digits once to make two 2-digit numbers.
    The total of the two numbers must be a multiple of 5.

Six friends each think of a number.

a Josh thinks of an odd number that is a multiple of 5.
The number is between 8 and 22.
What is Josh's number?

b Anna thinks of a square number between 30 and 40.
What is Anna's number?

c Filip thinks of an odd two-digit number bigger than 30.
One digit is double the other. What is Filip's number?

d Jan thinks of a two-digit number that is divisible by 5.
When its digits are reversed, the new number is 27
more than Jan's number. What is Jan's number?

e Mark thinks of a number between 20 and 30.
When he divides his number by 3, the remainder is 1.
When he divides his number by 4, the remainder is 2.
What is Mark's number?

f Holly thinks of a number that is a multiple of 3 and a multiple of 4.
The sum of its two digits is 9. What is Holly's number?

Extension problem

8 Copy and complete this diagram for the numbers from 30 to 60.

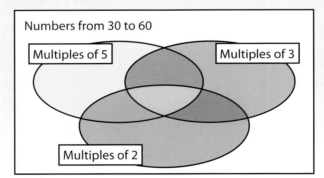

Numbers from 30 to 60

Multiples of 5

Multiples of 3

Multiples of 2

Points to remember

- A **multiple** of 5 is a number that divides exactly by 5.
- A number is a multiple of **2** if its last digit is even.
- A number is a multiple of **3** if its digit sum is a multiple of 3.
- A number is a multiple of **4** if half of it is even.
- A number is a multiple of **5** if its last digit is 0 or 5.
- A number is a multiple of **10** if its last digit is 0.

3 Positive and negative integers

This lesson will help you to put positive and negative numbers in order and work out temperature differences.

 Did you know that...?

Negative numbers were used in India in the 7th century to show debts.

Negative numbers were not used in Europe until the 15th century. In France, they were first called 'absurd numbers'.

Exercise 3

Integers are positive and negative whole numbers and zero.
Negative numbers have a minus sign in front of them.

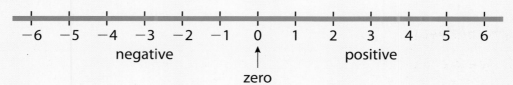

Example 1   Work out $-5 + 4$.

Start on -5 and move 4 to the right.

$-5 + 4 = -1$

Example 2   Work out $4 - 7$.

Start on 4 and move 7 to the left.

$4 - 7 = -3$

We use negative numbers for **temperatures below zero** in degrees Celsius.

$-5\,°C$ means 5 degrees below $0\,°C$. Temperatures above $0\,°C$ do not usually have a $+$ sign.

Example 3

Put these temperatures in order.

$-2\,°C$ $4\,°C$ $-3\,°C$ $3\,°C$ $0\,°C$

Start with the lowest temperature.

The correct order is:

$-3\,°C$ $-2\,°C$ $0\,°C$ $3\,°C$ $4\,°C$

Example 4

At midnight the temperature was $-3\,°C$.
At midday it had risen by 5 degrees.
What was the temperature at midday?

Start at -3. Count up 5.
The temperature at midday was $2\,°C$.

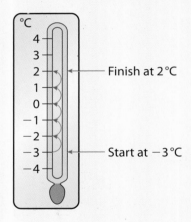

Example 5

The temperature fell from $3\,°C$ to $-1\,°C$.
How many degrees did the temperature fall?

Start at 3. Count down to -1.
The temperature fell by 4 degrees.

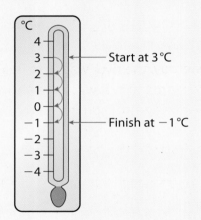

---

1   Look at these temperatures.

   $-2\,°C$ $3\,°C$ $-7\,°C$ $-1\,°C$ $-5\,°C$

   a   Which temperatures are below freezing?

   b   Which temperature is nearest to $0\,°C$?

   c   Write the temperatures in order, coldest first.

2   At dawn, the temperature was $-3\,°C$.
   By midday, the temperature was $7\,°C$.
   By how much did the temperature rise?

3 The temperature in London was −2 °C.
In Inverness it was −7 °C.
How many degrees colder was it in Inverness than in London?

4 The table shows the highest and lowest January temperatures for seven cities.
Find the difference between the highest and lowest temperatures for each city.

City	Highest temperature (°C)	Lowest temperature (°C)
Belfast	5	−4
Liverpool	8	−2
Cardiff	7	−3
Newcastle	3	−6
London	8	−2
Plymouth	10	−1
York	4	−5

5 Yesterday, the river was 8 cm below sea level.
After some rain, it was 3 cm above sea level.
By how many centimetres did the water level rise?

6 Small stars show how long food can be stored in a freezer.

		Storage times for frozen food
★	−6 °C	up to 1 week
★★	−12 °C	up to 1 month
★★★	−18 °C	up to 3 months

Find the difference between these storage temperatures.

a ★★ and ★ b ★★★ and ★★ c ★★★ and ★

7 Use a number line to help you.

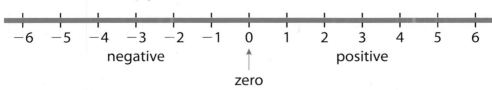

a −5 + 2 b −6 + 7 c −3 + 3 d 4 − 5
e −6 + 10 f 0 − 5 g 6 − 10 h −1 − 4

8 Copy and complete these.

a $-4 + \square = -2$ b $-3 + \square = 1$ c $5 - \square = -2$

d $-2 - \square = -6$ e $\square - 4 = -2$ f $\square + 3 = 2$

Extension problem

9 This is a magic square.
Each row adds up to 0.
Each column adds up to 0.
Each diagonal adds up to 0.

Copy the square.
Fill in the missing numbers.

-3	...	...
2	0	...
1	...	3

 Points to remember

- The **negative number** -6 is 'negative 6'.
- -10 is less than -5.
- Six degrees below zero is minus six degrees Celsius ($-6\,°C$).
- $-10\,°C$ is a lower temperature than $-5\,°C$.
- Always include the units when you write a temperature.

How well are you doing?

Can you:

- work out square numbers?
- spot multiples of one-digit numbers?
- test numbers to see if they divide exactly by 2, 3, 4, 5 or 10?
- put positive and negative numbers in order?
- work out temperature differences across 0 °C?

Properties of numbers (no calculator)

1 *2000 Mental Test level 4*

Two of these numbers are multiples of 7. Which numbers are they?

18   22   28   32   35

2 *2003 level 4*

When the wind blows it feels colder. The stronger the wind, the colder it feels.

Write a temperature to go in each of the spaces **A**, **B** and **C**.

Wind strength	Temperature out of the wind (°C)	How much colder it feels in the wind	Temperature it feels in the wind (°C)
Moderate breeze	5	7 degrees colder	−2
Fresh breeze	−8	11 degrees colder	**A**
Strong breeze	−4	**B** degrees colder	−20
Gale	**C**	23 degrees colder	−45

3 *2004 Mental Test level 4*

What is the next number in the sequence of square numbers?

1   4   9   16   …

(4) *2004 KS2 level 4*

Here is a sorting diagram for numbers.

Write a number less than 100 that could go in each of the spaces **A**, **B**, **C** and **D**.

	Even	Not even
A square number	A	B
Not a square number	C	D

Properties of numbers (calculator allowed)

(5) *2006 Progress Test level 3*

a The first odd number is 1.
  What is the sixth odd number?

b The first five odd numbers add up to 25.
  What do the first six odd numbers add up to?

(6) *2003 Progress Test level 3*

a The temperature was $-10\,°C$.
  It went up by 15 degrees.
  What is the new temperature?

b Write these temperatures in order, starting with the coldest.

  $-3\,°C$ $0\,°C$ $6\,°C$ $-9\,°C$

(7) *2006 KS2 level 4*

Here is a sorting diagram with four sections, **A**, **B**, **C** and **D**.

	Multiple of 10	Not a multiple of 10
Multiple of 20	A	B
Not a multiple of 20	C	D

a Write a number that could go in section C.

b Section **B** can never have any numbers in it.
  Explain why.

Graphs, charts and tables

This unit will help you to:

- draw and interpret data in tally charts, bar charts, pictograms, and Venn and Carroll diagrams;
- find and use the mode and range of a set of data.

1 Tally charts, bar charts and pictograms

This lesson will help you to draw and interpret tally charts, bar charts and pictograms.

Exercise 1

A **tally chart** helps you to sort and count data

It uses special marks called **tally marks**.

Tally chart: Class 7H favourite sandwich fillings

Filling	Tally	Frequency
Egg	III	3
Cheese	IIII IIII	10
Tuna	IIII	5
Ham	IIII III	8
Prawn	IIII	4

A **bar chart** uses bars to show data.

Label both axes to say what they show.

Number the grid lines of the frequency axis.

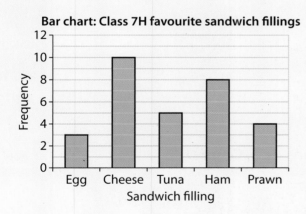

Bar chart: Class 7H favourite sandwich fillings

A **pictogram** uses symbols to show data.

A key tells you how many items each symbol stands for.

The symbols are the same size and lined up neatly.

Pictogram: Class 7H favourite sandwich fillings

Filling	
Egg	🧍🧍
Cheese	🧍🧍🧍🧍🧍
Tuna	🧍🧍🧍
Ham	🧍🧍🧍🧍
Prawn	🧍🧍

Key: 🧍 = 2 people

You will need graph paper, a sharp pencil and a ruler.

1   This graph shows the numbers of pupils in a class who had a school lunch on different days of the week.

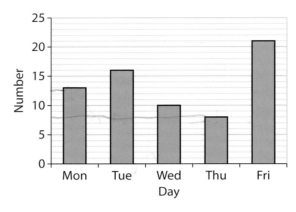

Copy and complete this table to show how many pupils had a school lunch each day.

Day	Monday	Tuesday	Wednesday	Thursday	Friday
Number					

2   This table shows how many pupils had school dinners in a large school during one week.

Day	Mon	Tues	Wed	Thurs	Fri
Number	65	27	63	77	54

a   Draw a bar chart to represent the data.
   The scale on the vertical axis should go from 0 to 100.
   Use 1 cm for every 10 pupils.

   Each bar should be 2 cm wide.
   Make a 1 cm gap between each bar.

b   Copy and complete this sentence.

   The bar chart shows that most pupils had school lunch on .... and fewest pupils had school lunch on ....

(3) Work with a partner.

Each of the tables P, Q and R matches one of the graphs, A, B or C.

Match each table to the correct graph.

The labels are missing from the bar charts to make it harder.

Table P

Eye colour	Frequency
Blue	2
Green	3
Black	6
Brown	5
Grey	1

Graph A

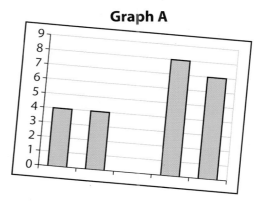

Graph B

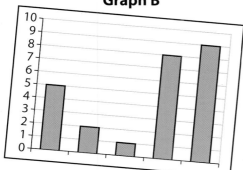

Table R

Front door colour	Frequency
Blue	4
Green	4
Black	0
Red	8
Grey	7

Table Q

Favourite colour	Frequency
Blue	5
Green	2
Yellow	1
Purple	8
Brown	9

Graph C

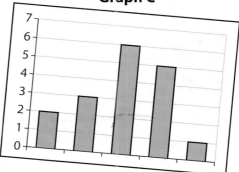

(4) This pictogram shows the eye colours of 40 people.

a How many people does one symbol represent?

b How many people have blue eyes?

c What is the most frequent eye colour?

d What is the least frequent eye colour?

Eye colour	
Blue	◯ ◯ ◖
Green	◯ ◿
Black	◯ ◯ ◯ ◯
Brown	◖
Grey	◯ ◔

Key: ◯ stands for 4 people

The tally chart shows 100 children's favourite drinks.

a Show this data in a pictogram.

Choose your own symbol to stand for ten children.

b How many more children prefer fruit juice than like lemonade?

c Copy and complete these sentences:

The pictogram shows that the most popular drink was ………

The next most popular drink was ………

Drink	Tally	Frequency
Water	卌 卌 卌	15
Lemonade	卌 卌 卌 卌	20
Cola	卌 卌 卌 卌 卌	25
Fruit juice	卌 卌 卌 卌 卌 卌 卌	35
Other	卌	5

Points to remember

⊙ A **tally chart** helps you to count and sort data using tally marks.

⊙ **Bar charts** and **pictograms** are ways of showing data.

⊙ The **frequency** is the total number in each category.

2 Venn and Carroll diagrams

This lesson will help you to use Venn and Carroll diagrams to sort data.

Did you know that...?

John Venn lived from 1834 to 1923. He was a lecturer at Cambridge University.

He is best known in mathematics for his way of showing data on a diagram.

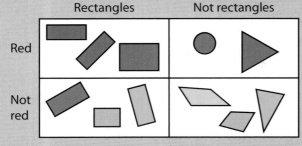

Carroll diagram

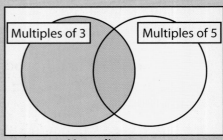

Venn diagram

Charles Dodgson was the real name of **Lewis Carroll**, who wrote *Alice's Adventures in Wonderland*. He taught mathematics at Oxford University.

In 1896, he invented a new way of showing sorted data, known as a Carroll diagram.

Example 1

Sort these numbers using a Carroll diagram.

37, 18, 49, 103, 15, 12, 52, 108

Use two properties:

whether they are even or not even, and
whether they are less than 50 or not.

	Even	Not even
Less than 50	18 12	37 49 15
Not less than 50	52 108	103

Example 2

Some shapes have been sorted on a Venn diagram.

a How many of the shapes are red and have four sides?

Two shapes: the red parallelogram and the red rectangle in the intersection.

b How many of the shapes are not red and do not have four sides?

Two shapes: the pink star and the yellow hexagon.

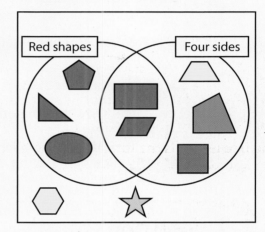

Work with a partner. You need **S2.1 Resource sheets 2.1 and 2.3 and a set of cards made from S2.1 Resource sheet 2.2.**

1 Put the cards 'Odd' and 'Not odd' across the top of the Carroll diagram on **S2.1 Resource sheet 2.1**.

Put the cards '**Multiple of 3**' and '**Not multiple of 3**' down the side so that it looks like this.

	Odd	Not odd
Multiple of 3		
Not a multiple of 3		

a Place the number cards in the right boxes.

b In your book, write all the card numbers that are odd and multiples of 3.

c How many of the card numbers are not odd and not multiples of 3?

2 Put 'Multiple of 5' and 'Not a multiple of 5' across the top of the Carroll diagram on S2.1 Resource sheet 2.1. Put 'Multiple of 4' and 'Not a multiple of 4' down the side.

	Multiple of 5	Not a multiple of 5
Multiple of 4		
Not a multiple of 4		

a Put the number cards in the right boxes.

b In your book, write all the card numbers that are multiples of 5 and multiples of 4.

c Which card numbers are multiples of 4 but not multiples of 5?

d Write five numbers that are not multiples of 4 and not multiples of 5.

3 Use the statement and number cards to make up two more Carroll diagrams.

4 Use S2.1 Resource sheet 2.3.

Label one circle 'Odd' and the other 'Less than 10'.

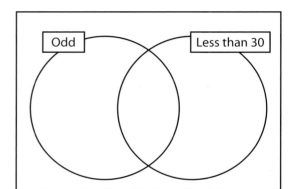

a Put the number cards in the right places on the diagram.

b In your book, write three more numbers that are odd and not less than 30.

5 Label one circle 'Multiple of 3' and the other 'Multiple of 5'.

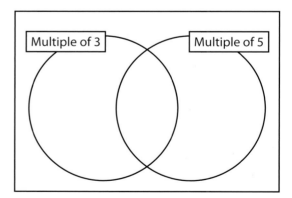

a Put the number cards in the right places on the diagram.

b Which number goes in the intersection? Why?

c Describe the numbers that are outside both circles.

Extension problem

6 Use the statement cards and number cards.
Make up two more Venn diagrams of your own.

3 Mode and range

This lesson will help you to work out the mode and range for a small set of data.

Exercise 3

The **mode** is the most common value in a set of data.

The **range** is found by subtracting the smallest value from the largest value in a set of data.

Example 1

Ali counted the number of cars of each colour in the staff car park. He recorded his results in a table.

What is the mode for the car colour?

The mode for car colour is silver because silver is the largest group.

Colour of car	Frequency
Red	7
Blue	6
Green	3
White	5
Silver	9
Black	2
Other	4

Example 2

These are the prices of an orange in ten different shops:

   8p,   12p,   9p,   11p,   10p,   11p,   9p,   11p,   12p,   11p

Find the mode and range.

The mode of the prices is 11p because this is the most common price.

The range of the prices is 12p − 8p = 4p.
This is the difference between the most expensive shop price and the cheapest.

1. Work in a group of four.
   You need some sets of 0–9 digit cards.

   ◎ Shuffle the digit cards.

   ◎ Take the top ten cards from the pile and spread them out face up.

   ◎ Write down the smallest digit and the largest digit.

   ◎ Use these to calculate the range for the group of cards.

   ◎ Which was the most common digit in your set of cards? This is the mode.

   Repeat these steps three more times.

2. Sheena is one of four children.
   They are aged 7, 9, 12 and 13.

   Elaine is one of five children.
   They are aged 4, 6, 7, 10 and 12.

   a What is the range of ages in Sheena's family?

   b What is the range of ages in Elaine's family?

   c Whose family has the biggest age range?

3. Iram counted the number of sweets in a jar.
   She recorded her results in a table.
   What is the mode for the colour of the
   sweets in the jar?

Colour of sweets	Frequency
Red	42
Orange	36
Yellow	42
Pink	51
Green	28
Black	50
Brown	47

4. Work out the mode and range for each of these sets of numbers.

   a 7, 8, 5, 4, 8, 9, 9, 5, 7, 9

   b 13, 17, 19, 21, 14, 15, 15, 18, 16, 17, 15, 12

   c 23, 24, 31, 19, 22, 24, 25, 28, 32

5 At the zoo, the keeper keeps records of the heights of penguins.

The heights of the penguins are:

37 cm, 46 cm, 38 cm, 41 cm, 40 cm,
41 cm, 39 cm, 41 cm, 38 cm, 43 cm

a Work out the mode of the penguin heights.

b Work out the range of the penguin heights.

c The zoo is given another penguin. It is 44 cm tall.
What is the range of the penguins' heights now?

6 Some children record how far they each can jump without a run-up:

86 cm, 77 cm, 75 cm, 75 cm, 62 cm, 75 cm, 81 cm, 88 cm, 73 cm

a How much further is the longest jump than the shortest jump?
What do we call this?

b What is the mode for the length of the jumps?

7 Here are the weights in tonnes (t) of eight elephants in a herd:

3.7 t, 5.1 t, 3.8 t, 6.2 t,
5.9 t, 4.4 t, 3.6 t, 4.5 t

Work out the mode and range for the weights of the elephants.

◉ Points to remember

⊙ The **mode** is the most common value in the set of data.

⊙ To find the **range** of a set of data, subtract the smallest value from the largest value.

How well are you doing?

Can you:

- interpret tally charts, bar charts, pictograms, Venn diagrams and Carroll diagrams?

- find the mode and range of a set of data?

1 *1995 level 3*

The pictogram shows the number of animals in a safari park.
Each animal in the pictogram stands for 10 animals in real life.

Animals in the safari park

Elephants

Birds

Zebras

a How many zebras are there in the park?

b How many elephants are there in the park?

c Tandy looked at the pictogram.
She thought there were 45 birds in the park.
Explain why Tandy was wrong.

② Copy the diagram.
Write each of these numbers in its correct place on your diagram:

55,   23,   70,   72,   81

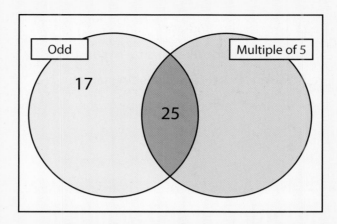

③ Copy the diagram.
Write each of these numbers in its correct place on your diagram:

8,   15,   24,   27,   26,   22,   20,   19

	Multiple of 4	Not a multiple of 4
Two-digit number	12	13
Not a two-digit number	4	6

④ The shoe sizes of ten children are:

5,   6,   9,   3,   6, $5\frac{1}{2}$,   6,   7,   8, $7\frac{1}{2}$

a What is the mode of their shoe sizes?

b What is the range of their shoe sizes?

Whole numbers

This unit will help you to:

- read, write, round and order numbers;
- multiply and divide numbers by 10 and 100;
- remember number facts, including tables;
- add, subtract, multiply and divide in your head and on paper;
- solve number problems.

1 Place value, ordering and rounding

This lesson will help you to read, write, round and order numbers.

Did you know that...?

About 4000 years ago, there was a country in the Middle East called **Babylonia**. The people built big cities. They had a legal system and even a postal service.

The **Babylonians** also had a number system. They counted in groups of **60**. Here are their first few numerals.

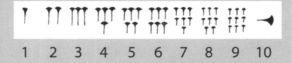

| 1 | 2 | 3 | 4 | 5 | 6 | 7 | 8 | 9 | 10 |

We still use the Babylonian way to measure time.
There are **60** seconds in 1 minute and **60** minutes in 1 hour.

Exercise 1

The number **6425** in words is **six thousand four hundred and twenty-five**.

Each digit has a different value.

Thousands	Hundreds	Tens	Units
6	4	2	5

Example 1   Write nine thousand and forty-three in figures.   9043

When you round numbers, look at the first unwanted digit.
If it is 5, 6, 7, 8 or 9, then add 1 to the last digit that you keep.
Then replace all the unwanted digits by zeros.

Example 2

What is 5624 to the nearest 10?

562**4** to the nearest 10 is 5620.

Example 3

What is 4867 to the nearest 100?

48**6**7 to the nearest 100 is 4900.

When you order whole numbers, look at the values of the digits.

Example 4

Put these five numbers in order.

246   72   678   8040   405

Start with the smallest number.

The smallest number is **7**2 because it has only **7 tens** and 2 units.

246, 678 and 405 all contain hundreds, tens and units.
246 has only **2 hundreds** so this is the next number.
405 has **4 hundreds** so this is the next number.
678 has **6 hundreds** so this is the next number.

8040 has **8 thousands** so this is the largest of the five numbers.

The correct order is 72, 246, 405, 678, 8040.

1   Write in figures:

a   forty-two thousand and six

b   ten thousand

c   twenty-three thousand and forty-eight

d   one hundred thousand

e   four thousand, eight hundred and twenty-four

f   eighteen thousand, four hundred and seven

g   two million

2   Write in words:

a   405   b   7050   c   40 300   d   6 000 000

③ Make the biggest possible number.
Use each digit once.

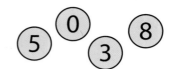

④ Make the smallest possible number.
Use each digit once.

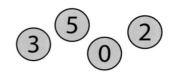

⑤ Write these in order. Start with the smallest number.

a 3663   6361   6311   6631

b 6206   6602   6262   6620

c 1818   1181   1881   1811

d 5333   3533   5353   5553

⑥ Write < or > between each pair of numbers.

a 222 … 22   b 7567 … 7657

c −5 … 5   d −12 … −15

⑦ Round to the nearest 10.

a 85   b 308   c 5912   d 477

⑧ Round to the nearest 100.

a 660   b 4320   c 7408   d 999

⑨ Round to the nearest 1000.

a 7567   b 9199   c 12 850   d 15 256

⑩ Play **Smaller and smaller** with a partner.
You need two packs of cards from 0 to 6 between you.

Rules

◉ Put the cards face down and shuffle them.

◉ Take turns to pick a card until you have four cards each.

◉ Make the smallest possible number with your four cards.
For example, with **0**, **2**, **3** and **2** you could make **2023**.

◉ The player with the smallest number wins a point.

◉ Put the cards back face down. Shuffle and pick again.

◉ The winner is the first to get 5 points.

Extension problem

 11 A box contains 300 paper clips.

    a What is the smallest number of paper clips that could be in the box?

    b What is the largest number of paper clips that could be in the box?

⦿ Points to remember

- ⊙ When you put numbers in order, look at the value of each digit.
- ⊙ $<$ means 'less than' and $>$ means 'more than'.
- ⊙ Round fives up. For example, 425 rounds to 430, and 650 rounds to 700.

2 Mental addition and subtraction

This lesson will help you to remember number facts and to add and subtract numbers in your head.

Exercise 2

Example

$63 - 38$

Use a number line. Start at 38. Count up to 63.

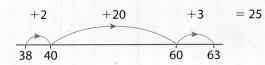

38 to 40 is **2**.
40 to 60 is **20**.
60 to 63 is **3**.
$2 + 20 + 3 = 25$
So $63 - 38 = 25$

1 You need seven number cards like these.

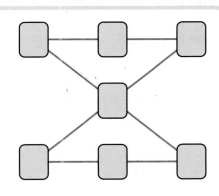

Arrange the cards as on the right.

Each line of three numbers must add up to 12.

Can you find another way to do it?

(2) Copy and complete the number sentences.
Use two of these numbers each time.

8   17   34   26   19

a   ... + ... = 42

b   ... − ... = 7

c   ... − ... = 18

d   ... + ... = 43

e   ... + ... = 36

f   ... − ... = 2

g   ... − ... = 8

h   ... + ... = 60

i   ... + ... = 27

j   ... − ... = 15

(3) Each letter of BIRTHDAY has a value.

B I R T H D A Y
5   7   9   11   13   15   17   19

In your head, add up the numbers in the words below.

a   HI

b   IT

c   AH

d   HAY

e   RIB

f   BAD

g   HID

h   ADD

i   RAT

Extension problem

This is an addition grid.
Each yellow number is the sum of
the orange number at the start of the row and
the orange number at the top of the column.

For example, 8 is the sum of 6 + 2.
5 is the sum of 1 + 4.

Copy and complete this addition grid.

+	2	3	4
6	8	9	10
1	3	4	5

+	14	10	…
…	…	36	…
…	…	27	48

Points to remember

- When you add numbers in your head, it is often easier to start with the larger number.
- Use an empty number line to record or explain mental methods.

3 Written methods

This lesson will help you to use written methods to add and subtract numbers.

Did you know that...?

In the Middle Ages, people used a **counting board** to help them to do sums.

They drew lines on a table or board.
They made counters for it.

This picture of a number game is from a
16th century maths textbook by Adam Riese.

One player is using numbers to help him
to work out answers. The other player is using
a counting board.

Exercise 3

You can add or subtract by writing numbers in columns.

Line up the units under the units, the tens under the tens, the hundreds under the hundreds, and so on.

Use rounding to estimate the answer.

Example 1   5269 + 437

Estimate: 5000 + 400 = 5400

```
  5269
+  437
 ─────
  5706
   1 1
```

Example 2   624 − 157

Estimate: 600 − 200 = 400
Count up from 157 to 624.

```
   624
 − 157
 ─────
    43  to make 200
   424  to make 624
   ───
   467
```

1 Copy and complete this table.

	Calculation	Estimate	Actual answer
a	88 + 43	90 + 40 = 130	131
b	468 + 317		
c	921 − 486		
d	2784 + 5814		
e	3321 − 867		

2 David has £381. He spends £236 on a TV.
How much does he have left?

3 Jamina has £547 in the bank. She pays in another £178.
How much does she now have in the bank?

4 Amy is going to Australia.

The air fare is £625. Amy has saved £538 towards it.
How much more does she need to save?

5. Daniel was born in 1984. How old will he be in 2030?

6. Vijay was born in 1938. When he is 85 years old, what year will it be?

7. Alison buys a new car for £8255. She trades in her old car for £4370.
    How much more does she have to pay for her new car?

8. There are 3118 people at a concert. 1473 of them are children.
    How many of the people are not children?

9. The sum of three numbers is 452. Two of the numbers are 147 and 286.
    What is the other number?

10. Shelly has £1250.
    She goes shopping for new furniture.
    She buys a sofa for £438.
    She buys a carpet for £380.
    She buys a lamp for £86.

    a   How much does Shelly spend altogether?

    b   How much does she have left?

Extension problems

11. Zoe has scored 34 846 on a pinball machine. She scores 8785 with her next ball.
    What is her new total score?

12. 9213 people vote in an election. They have one vote each.
    2347 people vote for John Cutts.
    3658 people vote for Mary Timms.
    The rest of the people vote for Abu Afzal.
    How many votes does Abu get?

◉ Points to remember

⊙ Look at the numbers before you decide what method to use for a
  calculation.

⊙ To add or subtract numbers, line up the digits in columns.
  Line up units under units, tens under tens, and so on.

4 Problem solving

This lesson will help you to use addition and subtraction to solve problems.

 Did you know that...?

In a **magic square**, the sum of the numbers in any row, column or diagonal is always the same.

The magic square was used in China 4000 years ago. Emperor Fuh-hi thought he saw a turtle with this pattern on its back.
The red spots in each row, column or diagonal add up to 15.

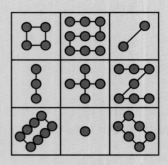

a magic square

Exercise 4

1. These are magic squares.
   The three numbers in each row, column and diagonal have the same total.

   Copy and complete these magic squares.

   a

6		
	5	3
		4

   b

10		
6		8
5		

   c

		10
	8	
6		5

2. Three darts land on this board.
   Darts in the outside ring score double that number.
   More than one dart can land in an area.

   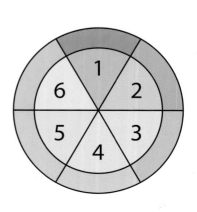

   Find different ways of scoring 26.
   How many different ways can you find?

3 You need a set of digit cards from 1 to 7.

Arrange your cards with + signs between them. Use each card once.

How close can you get to a total of 100?

Here is an example.

$$5\;2 + 1\;3 + 4\;6 + 7 = 118$$

Can you get closer to 100?

 Did you know that...?

Sudoku is a maths puzzle. **Howard Garns**, an American, invented it in 1979. In 1986 it became popular in Japan. It was given the name Sudoku.

Nearly every newspaper includes a Sudoku puzzle.

In this Sudoku puzzle each number 1, 2, 3 and 4 must appear once in each row, once in each column and once in each 2 by 2 square.

In this Sudoku puzzle, work out why the number in the top-left square must be 1.

	3		
2			
		1	
	1		3

Extension problem

4 Copy these Sudoku puzzles on squared paper. Fill in the missing numbers.

a

2			
	3	4	
			3
	2		

b

4	1		
		4	
	4		
			3

c

3		2	
		4	
			4
	2		1

5 Multiplying and dividing by 10, 100 and 1000

This lesson will help you to multiply and divide by 10, 100 and 1000.

Exercise 5

When you **multiply** a number:	**Examples**	
by **10**, its digits move **1 place to the left**;	56×10	560
by **100**, its digits move **2 places to the left**;	56×100	5600
by **1000**, its digits move **3 places to the left**.	56×1000	56 000

When you **divide** a whole number or decimal:		
by **1000**, its digits move **3 places to the right**;	$75\,000 \div 1000$	75
by **100**, its digits move **2 places to the right**;	$75\,000 \div 100$	750
by **10**, its digits move **1 place to the right**.	$75\,000 \div 10$	7500

1 Copy and complete.

   a $46 \times 100 = \ldots$ b $83 \times \ldots = 830$

   c $250 \times \ldots = 2500$ d $320 \times 100 = \ldots$

   e $5 \times 1000 = \ldots$ f $30 \times 10 = \ldots$

   g $40 \times \ldots = 4000$ h $10 \times \ldots = 1000$

2 Copy and complete.

   a $720 \div 10 = \ldots$ b $9100 \div \ldots = 91$

   c $550 \div \ldots = 55$ d $5000 \div 100 = \ldots$

   e $37\,000 \div 1000 = \ldots$ f $3700 \div 10 = \ldots$

   g $44\,000 \div \ldots = 4400$ h $3000 \div \ldots = 30$

(3) Copy and complete.

a 6050 ÷ 10 = ...

b 4000 ÷ 1000 = ...

c 51 × ... = 5100

d 3200 × 1000 = ...

e 82 000 ÷ 100 = ...

f 830 ÷ ... = 83

(4) This is what you need to make 1 fruit cake.

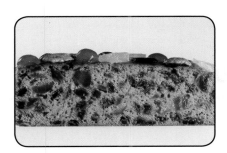

Fruit cake
200 g flour
100 g sugar
50 g margarine
80 g mixed fruit
3 eggs

Write a list of what you need to make 10 fruit cakes.

(5) Peter is paid £140 for 10 hours of gardening each weekend.

a How much is he paid for 1 hour of gardening?

b How much will he earn for gardening in 10 weekends?

(6) How many lengths of 10 centimetres can you cut from 100 metres of wire?

(7) Janet is a waitress at a hotel.
At breakfast she pours 100 ml of orange juice for each guest.
This morning she used exactly 10 litres of orange juice.
How many guests had a glass of orange juice?

(8) A **million** is 1 000 000, or 1 followed by 6 zeros.
Use the Internet to find out what these numbers are: **billion**, **trillion**, **googol**.

 Points to remember

⊙ When a number is:
× **10**, its digits move **1** place to the left;
× **100**, its digits move **2** places to the left;
× **1000**, its digits move **3** places to the left.

⊙ When a number is:
÷ **10**, its digits move **1** place to the right;
÷ **100**, its digits move **2** places to the right;
÷ **1000**, its digits move **3** places to the right.

6 Multiplication tables

This lesson will help you to double and halve numbers and to remember times tables.

 Did you know that...?

People have learned multiplication tables for thousands of years.

The **Babylonians** recorded this multiplication table on clay over 3000 years ago.

You can use facts you know to work out facts you can't remember.

Example

What is 8 × 9?

2 × 9 = 18	two nines are 18
so 4 × 9 = 36	four nines are double two nines
and 8 × 9 = 72	eight nines are double four nines

1. Jot down the answer to each part. Then write the total.
   a Add 5 × 7 to 3 × 8.
   b Add 10 × 6 to 4 × 6.
   c Add 4 × 8 to 9 × 4.
   d Add 3 × 7 to 5 × 9.
   e Add 6 × 7 to 4 × 9.
   f Add 6 × 8 to 7 × 7.

2. Jot down the answer to each part. Then write the difference.
   a Subtract 6 × 5 from 7 × 6.
   b Subtract 4 × 5 from 9 × 6.
   c Subtract 2 × 8 from 8 × 5.
   d Subtract 4 × 9 from 7 × 7.
   e Subtract 5 × 9 from 7 × 8.
   f Subtract 6 × 6 from 9 × 9.

3. Write the answers.
   a 4 × 20
   b 6 × 70
   c 40 × 8
   d 50 × 9
   e 5 × 600
   f 300 × 4
   g 8 × 700
   h 600 × 9
   i 20 × 40
   j 50 × 80
   k 90 × 40
   l 60 × 50

4 Look at this multiplication grid.   Copy and complete this grid.

×	4	7
5	20	35
8	32	56

×	2		7
		15	35
8			
	20		

Each yellow number is the product of the purple number at the start of the row and the purple number at the top of the column.

For example, 56 is 8 × 7.

5 Play **Sevens** with a partner.
You need two dice between you.

Rules

◉ Each player draws a 3 by 3 grid.

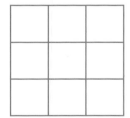

◉ Take turns to roll the two dice. Each spot is worth 7.

◉ Write your score on your grid.

◉ Carry on until your grid is full of numbers.

◉ Now take turns to roll the dice again.

◉ If the score is the same as a number on either player's grids, you can cross out that number.

◉ The winner is the first player to cross out all their numbers.

If you play the game again, make each spot worth 8 (or 9).

(6) Copy and complete.

a Make a total of 12. Put 2 or 3 in each box.

12 = □ + □ + □ + □ + □

b Make a total of 13. Put 2 or 5 in each box.

13 = □ + □ + □ + □ + □

c Make a total of 17. Put 3 or 4 in each box.

17 = □ + □ + □ + □ + □

d Make a total of 22. Put 4 or 5 in each box.

22 = □ + □ + □ + □ + □

e Make a total of 36. Put 7 or 8 in each box.

36 = □ + □ + □ + □ + □

Extension problem

(7) Draw two squares.

Write each of these numbers in one of the squares.
Use each number once.

1 2 3 4 5 6 7

The total in the big square must be six times the total in the small square.

Find two different ways to do it.

Points to remember

⊙ 5 times a number is half 10 times the number.
20 times a number is double 10 times the number.

⊙ 4 times a number is double 2 times the number.
6 times a number is double 3 times the number.
8 times a number is double 4 times the number.

⊙ 9 times a number is 10 times the number, minus the number.

⊙ 7 times a number is 5 times the number, plus 2 times the number.

7 Multiplication

This lesson will help you to multiply numbers and to solve multiplication problems.

Exercise 7

There are different ways to multiply numbers. Use an efficient method that works best for you.

Some people use a **grid method.**
If one number has more digits than the other, put it in the left-hand column.

Example 1   36 × 47

Estimate: 40 × 50 = 2000

×	30	6
40	1200	240
7	210	42

$$
\begin{array}{r}
1200 \\
240 \\
210 \\
+ 42 \\
\hline
1692
\end{array}
$$

Answer: 36 × 47 = 1692

Example 2   327 × 8

Estimate: 300 × 8 = 2400

×	8
300	2400
20	160
7	56
	2616

Answer: 327 × 8 = 2616

1 Solve these.

a Daisy is paid £6 for each hour she works.
How much is she paid for 35 hours?

b A bus has seats for 54 passengers.
How many passengers can sit on 9 buses?

c 7 friends fly to Greece for a holiday.
Each return ticket costs £138.
What is the total cost of the tickets?

d A glass of cola holds 285 millilitres.
How much cola is there in 3 glasses?

e It costs £23 per night to stay at a campsite.
What does it cost to stay for 14 nights?

f A shop sold 67 video games at £35 each.
How much money did the shop take for them?

g A crate holds 48 bottles of water.
How many bottles of water can 26 crates hold?

(2) Choose three different numbers from this set.
Multiply them together.

4 6 7 8 9

a You can get six different answers.
Find them all.

b Write the six answers in order from the smallest to the largest.

(3) Work out the missing numbers. Use the first line to help you.

a 14 × 15 = 210
14 × ... = 420

b 28 × 22 = 616
28 × 11 = ...

c 23 × 18 = 414
23 × 19 = ...

d 25 × 25 = 625
25 × ... = 600

(4) Play **Products** with a partner.
You need these cards between you.

2 3 4 5 6 7 8 9

Rules

○ Shuffle the cards. Put them in a pile face down.

○ Take turns to pick up three cards each.

○ Use your three cards to make a product like this.

 ×

○ Work out your product.

○ The player with the biggest product wins a point.

○ Return the cards to the pack. Shuffle them and pick again.

○ The winner is the first player to get 8 points.

Extension problem

 5 Use all the digits 1 to 6.

   1   2   3   4   5   6

Write one number in each circle to make
the calculation correct.

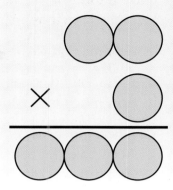

⦿ Points to remember

- ⊙ Use multiplication facts you know to work out others.
- ⊙ Using a grid can help you to multiply.
- ⊙ When you multiply, estimate the answer first.
- ⊙ Check your answer against the estimate.
- ⊙ Check your answer is sensible for the problem.

8 Division

This lesson will help you to divide numbers and solve division problems.

Exercise 8

There are different ways to divide numbers. Use an efficient method that works well for you.

Example

Work out $96 \div 6$.

How many sixes are there in 96?
10 sixes are 60, which is not enough.
20 sixes are 120, which is too many.
So the answer will be between 10 and 20 sixes.

```
  6)96
  −60   10 sixes      start by taking away 10 sixes
   36
  −36    6 sixes      take away the remaining 6 sixes
    0   16 sixes
```

Answer: $96 \div 6 = 16$

(1) Solve these.

a Sam earns £84 for 7 hours work.
   How much does he earn in an hour?

b £72 is shared equally among 3 people.
   How much money does each person get?

c A ticket for a ride at a theme park costs £5.
   Ticket sales for one day were £75.
   How many tickets for the ride were sold?

(2) Do these. Think whether to round your answer up or down.

a A jar of coffee contains 53 spoonfuls of coffee.
   A mug of coffee needs 2 spoonfuls of coffee.
   How many mugs of coffee can be made from the jar?

b A tin of tuna makes 5 sandwiches.
   James has to make 68 tuna sandwiches.
   How many tins of tuna should he buy?

c Megan is packing 68 tins into boxes.
   Each box holds 6 tins.
   How many full boxes can she pack?

d 60 pupils in Year 7 are going in mini-buses to the theatre.
   Each mini-bus can seat 9 pupils.
   How many mini-buses are needed?

e Suzy is buying cans of cola.
   She needs 90 cans.
   The cans are sold in packs of 8.
   How many packs should she buy?

f At a disco, 6 people can sit at a table.
   80 people are coming to the disco.
   How many tables will be full up?

g CDs cost £7 each.
   How many CDs can I buy with £100?

3 Play **Remainders** with a partner.
You need a dice and these cards between you.

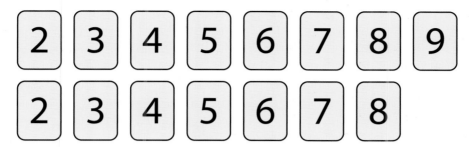

Rules

○ Shuffle the cards. Put them face down in a pile.

○ Take turns. Roll the dice.
If you roll 1, it counts as 7.

○ Take the top two cards from the pile and make a two-digit number.
For example, if you take 3 and 6, you can make 36 or 63.

○ Divide your two-digit number by the number you rolled.

○ The remainder is your score for that turn. Write it down.
Look out – the remainder might be 0!

○ Put your two cards back at the bottom of the pile.

○ It is now the other player's turn.

○ The winner is the first player to get a total score of 20.

● Points to remember

⊙ Set out calculations carefully.
⊙ When you divide, estimate the answer first.
⊙ Check your answer against the estimate.
⊙ Check your answer is sensible for the problem.
⊙ Decide whether to round the answer up or down.

How well are you doing?

Can you:

- read, write, round and order numbers?
- multiply and divide numbers by 10 and 100?
- remember number facts, including tables?
- add, subtract, multiply and divide numbers in your head and on paper?
- solve number problems?

Whole numbers and calculations (no calculator)

1 *2005 Progress Test level 3*

Copy and complete these calculations.

a $46 + \square = 73$

b $55 - \square = 29$

2 *2003 Progress Test level 3*

Work out the answers to these calculations.

a $257 + 649$

b $541 - 382$

3 *2005 Progress Test level 3*

A school raised £1758 for charity.

A newspaper wrote:

School raises nearly £1800 for charity

Copy this sentence and fill in the missing number.

The newspaper rounded £1758 to the nearest ...

(4) *2005 Progress Test level 4*

  a Which of the numbers below is four thousand and seven? Write it in your book.

  47   407   4007

  40 007   400 007

  b Write in figures the number three million.

(5) *2005 Progress Test level 4*

Work out the answers to these calculations.

a 6×25 **b** 16×25

(6) *Year 7 Optional Test level 4*

In one school year, Chris goes to school for 39 weeks.
In each of the weeks, he goes to 34 lessons.

How many lessons is that altogether?
Show your working.

(7) *Year 7 Optional Test level 4*

  a Work out:

   i $693 + 287 =$ **ii** $1093 - 718 =$

  b Divide 252 by 7.

(8) *2006 level 4*

Work out the missing numbers.
In each part, you can use the first line to help you.

a
$$16 \times 15 = 240$$
$$16 \times \ldots = 480$$

b
$$46 \times 44 = 2024$$
$$46 \times 22 = \ldots$$

c
$$600 \div 24 = 25$$
$$600 \div \ldots = 50$$

Patterns and sequences

This unit will help you to:

- ⊙ continue a sequence of numbers;
- ⊙ use a rule to make a sequence of numbers;
- ⊙ recognise multiples, factors and prime numbers.

1 Continuing sequences

This lesson will help you continue sequences.

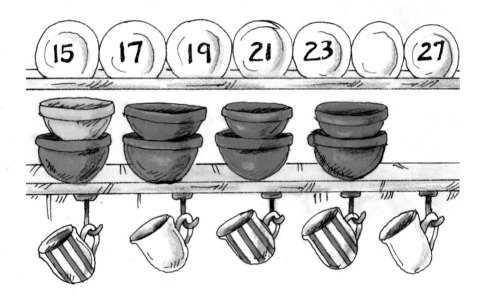

Exercise 1

A **sequence** of numbers or shapes follows a **rule**.

Here is a sequence of shapes using triangles.

  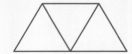 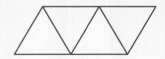

Pattern 1   Pattern 2   Pattern 3   Pattern 4
1 triangle   2 triangles   3 triangles   4 triangles

The rule to find the next pattern is 'add an extra triangle'.

This sequence of numbers follows the **rule** 'add 2'.

$$2, \quad 4, \quad 6, \quad 8, \quad 10, \quad \ldots$$

The numbers in the sequence are called **terms**.

The 1st term is 2. The 2nd term is 4. The 5th term is 10.
The next term is $10 + 2 = 12$.

The numbers are in **ascending** order. The sequence is **increasing**.

This sequence of numbers follows the **rule** 'subtract 5'.

$$30, \quad 25, \quad 20, \quad 15, \quad 10, \quad \ldots$$

The numbers are in **descending** order. The sequence is **decreasing**.

The 1st term is 30. The 2nd term is 25. The 5th term is 10.
The next term is $10 - 5 = 5$.

① Write the next three terms of each sequence.

a 1, 6, 11, 16, 21, ..., ..., ...

b 3, 7, 11, 15, 19, ..., ..., ...

c 95, 98, 101, 104, 107, 110, ..., ..., ...

d 100, 88, 76, 64, 52, ..., ..., ...

e 164, 160, 156, 152, 148, 144, ..., ..., ...

② Write the rule for each sequence.
Then find the next three terms of each sequence.

a 2, 12, 22, 32, 42, 52, ..., ..., ...

b 1, 9, 17, 25, 33, 41, ..., ..., ...

c 150, 143, 136, 129, 122, ..., ..., ...

d 99, 93, 87, 81, 75, 69, ..., ..., ...

e 2, 14, 26, 38, 50, 62, ..., ..., ...

3 Look at this sequence of numbers.

$$4, \quad 9, \quad 14, \quad 19, \quad 24, \quad 29, \quad 34, \quad 39, \quad \ldots$$

a What is the 1st term?

b What is the 4th term?

c What is the 8th term?

d Find the difference between the 1st term and the 2nd term.

e Find the difference between the 2nd term and the 3rd term.

f Write the next three terms of the sequence.

4 For each sequence, write whether it is **ascending** or **descending**.

a 1, 12, 23, 34, 45, ...

b 3, 18, 33, 48, 63, ...

c 98, 90, 82, 74, 66, ...

d 5, 4, 3, 2, 1, 0, ...

5 Draw the next pattern for each of these sequences.

a 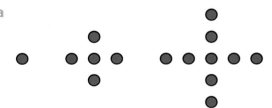 b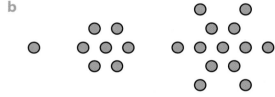

6 Look at this sequence of beads.
The 1st bead is yellow.
The 2nd bead is red.
The 3rd bead is blue.

a What colour is the 10th bead?

b What colour is the 30th bead? Explain how you know.

c What colour is the 31st bead? Explain how you know.

Extension problem

 Look at this sequence of numbers.

$$7, \quad 15, \quad 23, \quad 31, \quad 39, \quad 47, \quad \ldots$$

a   What is the difference between each term and the next one?

b   Write the rule for the sequence.

c   What is the 10th term?

d   What is the 20th term?

Points to remember

- A **sequence** of numbers follows a rule.
- Each number in a sequence is a **term**.
- The sequence 1, 3, 5, 7, … is in **ascending** order so it is **increasing**.
- The sequence 50, 47, 44, 41, 38, … is in **descending** order so it is **decreasing**.

2 Sequences from rules

This lesson will help you to generate a sequence given a term-to-term rule.

 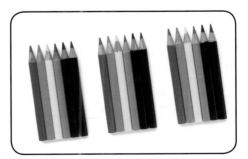

Exercise 2

If you know the first term of a sequence and the **rule**, you can make the sequence.

In a sequence, the first term is 6. The rule is 'add 9'. So the sequence is:

$$6, \quad 15, \quad 24, \quad 33, \quad 42, \quad 51, \quad \ldots$$

In a sequence, the first term is 87. The rule is 'subtract 5'. So the sequence is:

$$87, \quad 82, \quad 77, \quad 72, \quad 67, \quad 62, \quad \ldots$$

1 Write the next five terms of each of these sequences.

	1st term	Term-to-term rule
a	1	add 3
b	8	add 10
c	76	subtract 2
d	68	subtract 8
e	7	add 11
f	2	add 15

2 Copy and complete each sequence.

a 1, 5, 9, 13, ☐, ☐, 25

b ☐, ☐, 5, 7, 9, 11, ☐

c 3, ☐, ☐, 21, 27, ☐, 39

d 98, 96, ☐, ☐, 90, 88, ☐

3 Make up three sequences. Write the rule. Write the first five terms.

4 Draw patterns with dots to show the first three terms of these sequences.

	1st term	Term-to-term rule
a	1	add 3
b	1	add 5
c	1	add 8

Extension problem

5 Write the first five terms of each of these sequences.

	1st term	Term-to-term rule
a	1	add 0.5
b	0.1	add 0.1
c	20	subtract 0.2
d	50	subtract 0.5

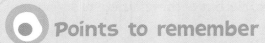

Points to remember

⊙ You can make a sequence if you know the **first term** and the **rule**.

For example, if the first term is 6 and the rule is 'add 4', the sequence is:

6, 10, 14, 18, 22, 26, …

3 Multiples

This lesson will help you to recognise multiples.

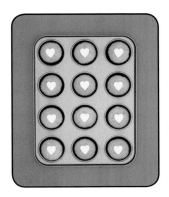

Exercise 3

This is the 8 times table.

8 × 1 = 8
8 × 2 = 16
8 × 3 = 24
8 × 4 = 32
8 × 5 = 40
8 × 6 = 48
8 × 7 = 56
8 × 8 = 64
8 × 9 = 72

8, 16, 24, 32, 40, 48, 56, 64, 72 are all **multiples of 8**.

80, 88, 96, 104, 112, 120, 128, … are also multiples of 8.

The **3rd** multiple of 8 is 8 × 3 = 24.

The **25th** multiple of 8 is 8 × 25 = 200.

The **100th** multiple of 8 is 8 × 100 = 800.

You need one copy each of **A2.1 Resource sheets 3.1 and 3.2**.

① Complete the multiplication square on **A2.1 Resource sheet 3.1**.

② Shade all the numbers on **A2.1 Resource sheet 3.2** that are multiples of 7.

3 **Use a calculator** to find out which of these numbers are multiples of 7.

252   1327   2989

4 Which of these numbers are multiples of 9?

153 - 161   756   230

5 a **Use a calculator** to check that 6129 is a multiple of 9.

b Add the digits $6 + 1 + 2 + 9$.

c Is the answer a multiple of 9?

d Add the digits of the answer. What do you notice?

e Which of these numbers are multiples of 9?

1206   2223   855

f Write a statement about multiples of 9.

g Which of these numbers have a remainder of 1 when they are divided by 9 ?

97	98	99
107	108	109
117	118	119

h Complete this three-digit number so that it is a multiple of 9.

2 ✱✱

6 a Describe this sequence of numbers.

6,   12,   18,   24,   30,   36,   ...

b What is the 4th term of the sequence?

c What is the 7th term of the sequence?

d What is the 10th term of the sequence?

e Write the rule for finding any term of the sequence.

a Describe this sequence of numbers.

4, 8, 12, 16, 20, 24, 28, 32, …

b Write a rule for finding any term of the sequence.

c Describe this sequence of numbers: 5, 9, 13, 17, 21, 25, 29, 33, …

d Write a rule for finding any term of the sequence.

 Points to remember

⊙ A **multiple** of a number divides exactly by that number.

4 Factors

This lesson will help you to find factors and prime numbers.

 Did you know that...?

Eratosthenes lived in Greece in 200 BC.

He found the prime numbers up to 100 by covering up 1, then all the numbers after 2 that are multiples of 2, then all the numbers after 3 that are multiples of 3, then all the numbers after 5 that are multiples of 5, then all the numbers after 7 that are multiples of 7.

The numbers that are left are prime numbers.

The method is called **Eratosthenes' sieve**.

1	2	3	4	5	6	7	8	9	10
11	12	13	14	15	16	17	18	19	20
21	22	23	24	25	26	27	28	29	30
31	32	33	34	35	36	37	38	39	40
41	42	43	44	45	46	47	48	49	50
51	52	53	54	55	56	57	58	59	60
61	62	63	64	65	66	67	68	69	70
71	72	73	74	75	76	77	78	79	80
81	82	83	84	85	86	87	88	89	90
91	92	93	94	95	96	97	98	99	100

Exercise 4

A **factor** is a number that divides exactly into another number.

The factors of 18 are 1, 2, 3, 6, 9, 18.

A **prime number** has exactly two factors, the number itself and 1.

Example   Write all the factors of 15 and 21.
What are the common factors of 15 and 21?

The factors of 15 are **1**, **3**, 5 and 15.   The factors of 21 are **1**, **3**, 7 and 21.

The common factors of 15 and 21 are 1 and 3 because they are in both lists.

1 Write all the factors of these numbers.

a	6	b	14	c	10	d	15	e	8
f	12	g	20	h	7	i	18	j	19

2 Which of these numbers are prime numbers?

a	2	b	10	c	5	d	9	e	11
f	15	g	4	h	3	i	1	j	6

3 What two numbers are factors of all even numbers?

4 Write the common factors of each pair of numbers.

a	10 and 15	b	8 and 24	c	7 and 21	d	9 and 21
e	6 and 10	f	15 and 25	g	12 and 20	h	14 and 10

Extension problem

5 Three prime numbers multiply together to make 231. What are they?

 Points to remember

- A **factor** of a number divides exactly into that number with no remainder.
  For example, the factors of 10 are 1, 2, 5, 10.

- A **prime number** has only two factors, 1 and itself.
  For example, 7 is a prime number because it has only two factors, 1 and 7.

5 Investigating patterns

This lesson will help you to investigate patterns.

Did you know that...?

Pythagoras was a Greek mathematician. He lived around 500 BC.

Pythagoras loved number patterns.

One of the interesting things he found out is:

$3^2 + 4^2 = 5^2$

Sequences of numbers can describe patterns.

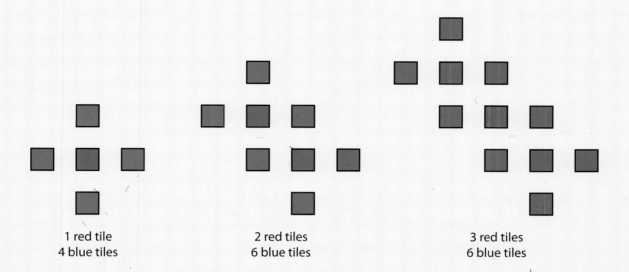

1 red tile
4 blue tiles

2 red tiles
6 blue tiles

3 red tiles
6 blue tiles

The sequence for the number of red tiles is 1, 2, 3, …
The next two patterns will have 4 then 5 red tiles.
The 10th pattern will have 10 red tiles.

The sequence for the number of blue tiles is 4, 6, 8, …
The next two patterns will have 10 then 12 blue tiles.
The 10th pattern will have 22 blue tiles.

 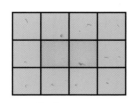 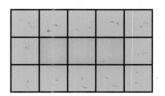

1st pattern

2nd pattern

3rd pattern

a   Write the sequence for the number of orange tiles.

b   How many orange tiles will be in the 4th pattern?

c   How many orange tiles will be in the 10th pattern?

d   Describe how the number of orange tiles increases each time.

e   Write the sequence for the number of blue tiles.

f   How many blue tiles will be in the 4th pattern?

g   How many blue tiles will be in the 10th pattern?

h   Describe how the number of blue tiles increases each time.

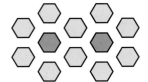 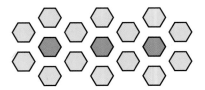

1st pattern   2nd pattern   3rd pattern

a Write the sequence for the number of purple tiles.

b How many purple tiles will be in the 4th pattern?

c How many purple tiles will be in the 6th pattern?

d Describe how the number of purple tiles increases each time.

e Write the sequence for the number of blue tiles.

f How many blue tiles will be in the 5th pattern?

g How many blue tiles will be in the 10th pattern?

h Describe how the number of blue tiles increases each time.

③

1st pattern   2nd pattern   3rd pattern   4th pattern

a Write the sequence for the number of dots in each pattern.

b How many dots will be in the 5th pattern?

c How many dots will be in the 10th pattern?

d Describe how the number of dots increases each time.

Extension problem

④

 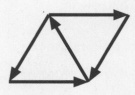 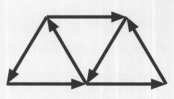

1 triangle   2 triangles   3 triangles

a How many arrows do you need to make 4 triangles?

b How many arrows do you need to make 10 triangles?

c How many arrows do you need to make 100 triangles?

d Explain how to work out how many arrows you need for 100 triangles.

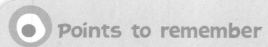

Points to remember

⊙ Work out a pattern made by shapes by looking at the way the pattern increases or decreases.

⊙ The number sequence helps you to work out how many shapes you need to make a pattern.

⊙ Finding a rule for working out the number of shapes needed saves time.

6 Making general statements

This lesson will help you to describe numbers and sequences.

Exercise 6

Example 1

Look at this number:

91

Write some statements to describe the number.

⊙ 91 is a two-digit odd number.

⊙ 91 lies between 80 and 100.

⊙ 7 and 13 are factors of 91.

Example 2

Look at this sequence:

2, 4, 6, 8, 10, 12, ...

a Describe the sequence.

⊙ All the numbers are even.

⊙ The sequence is increasing because the terms are in ascending order.

b What is the 10th term of the sequence?

The 10th term is $2 \times 10 = 20$.

c What is the 100th term of the sequence?

The 100th term is $2 \times 100 = 200$.

1 **a** What is this number?

Clues

- The number is even.
- It is less than 50.
- It is greater than 35.
- 3 is not a factor.
- It is a multiple of 10.

b What is this number?

Clues

- The number is odd.
- It is less than 30.
- It is a multiple of 5.
- It is greater than 10.
- 3 is a factor of the number.

c What is this number?

Clues

- The number is less than 90.
- It is greater than 50.
- It is even.
- It is a multiple of 5.
- 4 is not a factor.

2 Describe each sequence.
Write the 10th term.

a 3, 6, 9, 12, 15, …

b 10, 20, 30, 40, 50, …

c 2, 4, 6, 8, 10, …

d 5, 10, 15, 20, 25, …

e 4, 8, 12, 16, 20, …

f 7, 14, 21, 28, 35, …

g 8, 16, 24, 32, 40, …

Extension problem

a Paul is thinking of a number.
His number is a multiple of 4.

Which of these is the true statement?

A Paul's number must be even.

B Paul's number must be odd.

C Paul's number could be odd or even.

Explain how you know.

b Holly is thinking of a different number.
Her number is a factor of 20.

Which of these is the true statement?

A Holly's number must be even.

B Holly's number must be odd.

C Holly's number could be odd or even.

Explain how you know.

Points to remember

⊙ Use what you know about numbers to describe a number or a sequence.

For example, in the sequence 3, 6, 9, 12, 15, … each number is a multiple of 3.

The 10th term is 3×10.

The 100th term is 3×100.

How well are you doing?

Can you:

- continue a sequence of numbers?
- find the rule for a sequence of numbers?
- use a rule to write a sequence of numbers?
- find multiples and factors of numbers?
- recognise prime numbers?

1 What is the rule for finding the next term in this sequence?

2, 7, 12, 17, 22, ...

2 The first term of a sequence is 2 and the rule is 'add 6'.
Write the first five terms of the sequence.

3 *2004 Paper 2 level 4*

a Copy the table.
For each number in the table, write a multiple of that number.
Each multiple must be between 100 and 130.
The first one is done for you.

Number	Multiple between 100 and 130
40	120
35	
27	

b Is 7 a factor of 140? Explain how you know.

4 Find the missing numbers in this sequence:

4, □, □, 13, 16, □, 22

5 *2005 Paper 2 level 4*

    a Is 3 a factor of 30? Explain how you know.

    b I am thinking of a number that is greater than 3.
       My number is a factor of 30.
       What could my number be? Give an example.

6 *2007 level 4*

    a A three-digit number is a multiple of 4.

       What could the number be?
       Give an example.

       Now give a different example.

    b A two-digit number is a factor of 100.

       What could the number be?
       Give an example.

       Now give a different example.

7 *2007 Progress test level 4*

    a Write a number that is both

greater than 10	and	a multiple of 4

    b Now write a number that is both

greater than 10	and	a square number

Fractions, decimals and percentages

This unit will help you to:

- find and compare fractions of shapes;

- find two fractions that add up to 1;

- work out fractions of numbers, money or measures;

- use decimals for tenths and hundredths;

- understand and work out percentages;

- recognise equivalent fractions, decimals and percentages.

1 Fractions of shapes

This lesson will help you to work out fractions of shapes and find two fractions that add up to 1.

Exercise 1

This shape is divided into seven equal triangles. $\frac{2}{7}$ is shaded blue. $\frac{5}{7}$ is shaded orange.

$$\frac{2}{7}$$

The top number shows that **2** parts of the shape are shaded.
The top number of the fraction is the **numerator**.

The bottom number shows that the shape is divided into **7** equal parts.
The bottom number of the fraction is the **denominator**.

1 Look at these shapes.

A    B 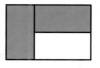   C 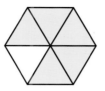   D

E   F   G 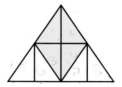   H

I 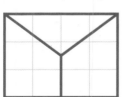   J    K 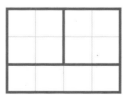   L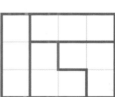

Copy and complete this table.

Shape	A	B	C	D	E	F	G	H	I	J	K	L
Shaded fraction	$\frac{1}{6}$											
Unshaded fraction												

2 For each shape, say whether it is divided into thirds. Write **Yes** or **No**.

a 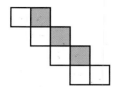   b 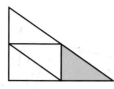   c

d 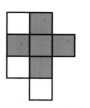   e 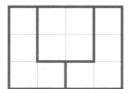   f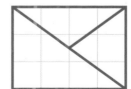

3 Copy and complete these.

a $\frac{1}{8} + \frac{7}{8} = \ldots$ b $1 - \frac{2}{3} = \ldots$

c $\frac{4}{9} + \ldots = 1$ d $1 - \frac{9}{10} = \ldots$

e $\frac{1}{4} + 1\frac{3}{4} = \ldots$ f $\ldots + \frac{5}{7} = 1$

4 a Jason drinks $\frac{3}{5}$ of a bottle of water. What fraction is left?

b Asif spent $\frac{3}{8}$ of his pocket money. What fraction does he have left?

c Jessie has a bag of flour.
She uses $\frac{3}{10}$ of the flour to make a cake.
What fraction of the flour is left?

d The home team scored $\frac{2}{3}$ of the goals in a match.
What fraction of the goals did the away team score?

e $\frac{5}{7}$ of the crowd support the home team.
What fraction supports the away team?

f $\frac{4}{5}$ of the players have dark hair.
What fraction does not have dark hair?

g The away team scored $\frac{5}{9}$ of the total number of goals.
What fraction of the goals did the home team score?

5 You need some squared paper.

This square is divided into 8 triangles.
Half of the square is coloured red.
Investigate other ways of colouring half of the square red.

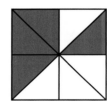

Extension problem

6 Tina chooses some square tiles. She wants $\frac{3}{5}$ of each tile she chooses to be blue.
Which of these square tiles could she choose?

      A   B   C   D   E

 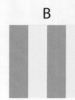 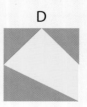  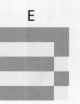

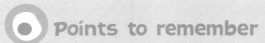

Points to remember

⊙ A fraction is a part of a whole.

The top number of a fraction is the **numerator**.
The bottom number is the **denominator**.

⊙ If a shape is divided into 8 equal parts, and 3 parts are shaded, then $\frac{3}{8}$ of the shape is shaded.

⊙ If $\frac{3}{8}$ of a shape is shaded, then $\frac{5}{8}$ is not shaded.

2 Equivalent fractions

This lesson will help you to work out fractions that are equivalent to each other.

Did you know that...?

As early as 1800 BC the Egyptians wrote fractions.

They put a picture of a mouth above a number to make it into a fraction with numerator 1.

The picture on the right meant $\frac{1}{5}$.

Exercise 2

Equivalent fractions are fractions that are equal.

These rectangles are all the same size.

One half of each rectangle is shaded.

The diagrams show that $\frac{1}{2}$, $\frac{2}{4}$ and $\frac{4}{8}$ are equivalent fractions.

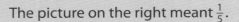

$$\frac{1}{2} \qquad\qquad \frac{2}{4} \qquad\qquad \frac{4}{8}$$

To **simplify** or **cancel** a fraction, divide the numerator and denominator by the same number.

To change a fraction to an **equivalent fraction**, multiply the numerator and denominator by the same number.

Example 1

Simplify $\frac{12}{20}$.

Divide the top and the bottom by 4.

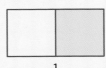

$$\frac{12}{20} = \frac{12 \div 4}{20 \div 4} = \frac{3}{5}$$

Example 2

How many eighths are equivalent to $\frac{3}{4}$?

Multiply the top and the bottom by 2.

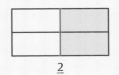

$$\frac{3}{4} = \frac{3 \times 2}{4 \times 2} = \frac{6}{8}$$

1. These diagrams tell you that three fractions are equivalent.
Which three fractions are they?

 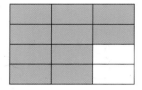 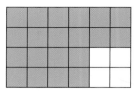

2. Use this diagram.

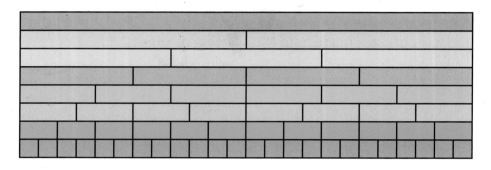

   a Write five different ways of writing $\frac{1}{2}$.

   b Write three different ways of writing $\frac{1}{4}$.

   c Write three different ways of writing $\frac{1}{3}$.

   d Write three different ways of writing $\frac{3}{4}$.

   e Write three different ways of writing $\frac{2}{3}$.

3. Write the shaded fraction of the hexagon in three different ways.

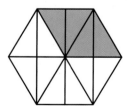

4. a Write three fractions that are equivalent to $\frac{2}{5}$.

   b Write three fractions that are equivalent to $\frac{3}{5}$.

   c Write three fractions that are equivalent to $\frac{4}{5}$.

5 Write each of these fractions as simply as you can.

a $\frac{4}{12}$ b $\frac{6}{8}$ c $\frac{5}{10}$ d $\frac{9}{12}$ e $\frac{4}{10}$

f $\frac{2}{8}$ g $\frac{15}{25}$ h $\frac{16}{20}$ i $\frac{25}{35}$

6 What fraction is each of these? Write each fraction as simply as you can.

a 3 out of 6 b 8 out of 12 c £15 out of £20

d 100 g out of 200 g e 50 m out of 200 m f 90 cm out of 100 cm

7 Play **Matching fractions** with a partner.
You need a set of cards made from **N2.3 Resource sheet 2.1**.

Rules

⊙ Spread the cards face down on the table. Shuffle them.

⊙ Take turns.

⊙ Turn over two cards.
If they are matching equivalent fractions, keep them and have another turn.

⊙ If they are not equivalent, turn them back face down.
It is then the other player's turn.

⊙ The winner is the player who wins the most pairs of cards.

⊙ **Points to remember**

⊙ To change a fraction to an equivalent fraction, multiply the numerator and the denominator by the same number.

⊙ To simplify a fraction, divide the numerator and the denominator by the same number. This is called 'cancelling'.

3 Fractions of quantities

This lesson will help you to find fractions of numbers, money or measures.

1 Work these out. Show your working.

  a $\frac{1}{2}$ of 18

  b $\frac{1}{4}$ of 28

  c $\frac{1}{10}$ of 80

  d $\frac{1}{8}$ of 40

  e $\frac{1}{9}$ of 54

  f $\frac{1}{100}$ of 600

  g $\frac{1}{3}$ of 36 kilograms

  h $\frac{1}{2}$ of 64 kilometres

  i $\frac{1}{5}$ of 45 minutes

2 a Sarah spends $\frac{1}{5}$ of her savings of £100. How much money does she spend?

  b One lap of a running track is 800 m.
    Mark runs $\frac{1}{4}$ of the distance.
    How far does he run?

  c Mark needs £90 to buy running shoes.
    He has saved $\frac{1}{3}$ of this.
    How much money does Mark still need?

  d $\frac{1}{8}$ of the 32 pupils in a class wear glasses.
    How many of the pupils wear glasses?

3 Work these out. Show your working.

a $\frac{2}{3}$ of 15

b $\frac{3}{4}$ of 48

c $\frac{4}{5}$ of 35

d $\frac{3}{10}$ of £90

e $\frac{2}{5}$ of 100 litres

f $\frac{3}{8}$ of 80 miles

g $\frac{5}{9}$ of 36 minutes

h $\frac{7}{10}$ of 30 seconds

i $\frac{4}{7}$ of 14 days

4 Play **Fraction strip** with a partner.
You need two dice.

Rules

◉ Each player should draw a strip of boxes like this.

◉ Each player should choose five different numbers from this list.

10   12   15   20   24   30   36   40   45   48   50

Write the five numbers in your boxes.

◉ Take turns to roll the dice. If the numbers are the same, roll again.

◉ Make a fraction. Use the smaller number as the numerator.
For example, if you roll 4 and 5, make the fraction $\frac{4}{5}$.

◉ Work out that fraction of 60.

◉ If the answer is on your strip, cross it out. If not, wait for your next turn.

◉ The winner is the first to cross out all the numbers on their strip.

5 Solve these problems. Show your working.

a Jody gets £24 pocket money each month.
She saves $\frac{3}{4}$ of it at the Post Office.
How much does she save each month?

b A bottle of squash contains 750 millilitres.
$\frac{2}{3}$ of the squash has been drunk.
How many millilitres have been drunk?

(6) Solve these problems. Show your working.

a There are 400 seats on a train.
$\frac{7}{8}$ of the seats are standard class.
Work out the number of standard class seats.

b There are 600 passengers on a train.
$\frac{3}{5}$ of them are male.
How many female passengers are there?

c William used to weigh 52 kg.
When he went on a diet, he lost $\frac{1}{10}$ of his weight.
How much does William weigh now?

d A full bottle of milk contains 375 millilitres.
$\frac{2}{5}$ of the milk has been used to make pancakes.
How many millilitres of milk have been used to make pancakes?

Extension problems

(7) Simon has £96 in savings.
He spent $\frac{1}{4}$ of his savings on a ticket for a match,
and $\frac{1}{3}$ of his savings on a computer game.
How much money does he have left?

(8) There are 525 girls and 475 boys in a school.
$\frac{2}{5}$ of the girls like football.
$\frac{3}{5}$ of the boys like football.
How many of the girls and boys like football?

◉ Points to remember

⊙ Find fractions of numbers by dividing. For example, to find one third, divide by 3.

⊙ To find one quarter, find one half of one half.

⊙ To find three quarters, first find one quarter, then multiply it by 3.

⊙ To find two thirds, first find one third, then multiply it by 2.

4 Decimal place value

This lesson will help you to understand place value in decimals.

Exercise 4

The **decimal point** separates the whole-number part from the part that is less than 1.

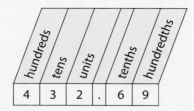

The first number after the decimal point tells us how many **tenths** there are.
The second number after the decimal point tells us how many **hundredths** there are.

The number shown above is 'four hundred and thirty-two point six nine'.

- ⊙ The 4 has a value of 4 hundreds.
- ⊙ The 3 has a value of 3 tens.
- ⊙ The 2 has a value of 2 units or ones.
- ⊙ The 6 has a value of 6 tenths.
- ⊙ The 9 has a value of 9 hundredths.

Example

What is the value of the 2 in the number 34.72?

The 2 has a value of 2 hundredths.

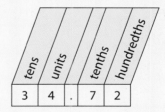

We can show decimals on a decimal number line.

Here is the number line from 2 to 3, labelled in **tenths**.

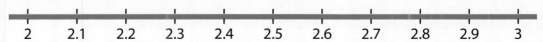

Here is the number line from 3.2 to 3.3, labelled in **hundredths.**

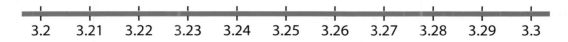

1. Copy and complete these.

   In 52.7

   a the 5 stands for ....

   b the 7 stands for ....

   In 46.02

   c the 2 stands for ....

   d the 0 stands for ....

   e the 6 stands for ....

2. Write these decimals as fractions.

   a 0.7   b 5.1   c 10.3

   d 1.9   e 0.5   f 26.01

   g 0.05   h 12.09   i 8.07

3. Write these fractions as decimals.

   a $\frac{1}{10}$ b $\frac{3}{10}$ c $\frac{5}{100}$

   d $4\frac{7}{10}$ e $12\frac{9}{10}$ f $3\frac{1}{100}$

   g $\frac{8}{100}$ h $17\frac{4}{100}$ i $14\frac{4}{10}$

4. What number is each arrow pointing to?

   a

   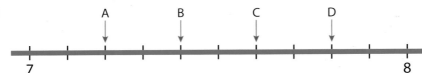

   b

   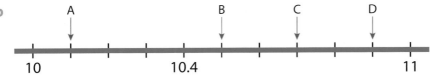

5. Estimate the numbers that the arrows are pointing to.

6 What number is each arrow pointing to?

a

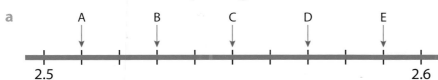

b

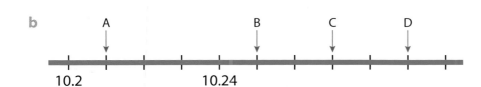

7 Write the next three terms in each sequence.

a 8.1   8.2   8.3   …   …   …

b 1.6   1.7   1.8   …   …   …

c 5.2   5.4   5.6   …   …   …

d 6.5   6.4   6.3   …   …   …

e 3.64   3.65   3.66   …   …   …

f 5.26   5.27   5.28   …   …   …

8 Play **Decimal track** with a partner. You need one dice.

Rules

⊙ Each of you starts with a score of 0.

⊙ Take turns to roll the dice.

If you roll 1, add 0.1 to your score.
If you roll 2, add 0.2 to your score.
If you roll 3, add 0.3 to your score.
If you roll 4, add 0.4 to your score.
If you roll 5, add 0.5 to your score.

If you roll 6, you miss that turn.

⊙ The winner is the first to reach 4.

⊙ Points to remember

⊙ The decimal point separates the whole number from the decimal fraction.

⊙ Each digit in a decimal number has a value based on its position.

⊙ The first decimal place is for tenths,
the second decimal place is for hundredths,
the third decimal place is for thousandths, and so on.

5 Tenths and hundredths

This lesson will help you to relate tenths to hundredths.

Exercise 5

£1 is equivalent to 100p. Each penny is one hundredth of £1.
£3.76 is £3 and 76p.

One tenth of £1

£0.10

One hundredth of £1

£0.01

You can think of 25p as two 10p coins and five 1p coins, or $\frac{2}{10}$ and $\frac{5}{100}$ of £1.

You can also think of 25p as twenty-five 1p coins, or $\frac{25}{100}$ of £1.

So $\frac{2}{10}$ and $\frac{5}{100}$ is equivalent to $\frac{25}{100}$, and 0.25 is equivalent to $\frac{25}{100}$.

A metre is divided into 100 centimetres.
Each centimetre is **one hundredth** of a metre.

A height of 1 metre and 34 centimetres is written as 1.34 metres or 1.34 m.
A height of 1 metre and 30 centimetres is written as 1.30 metres or 1.3 m.

A centimetre is divided into 10 millimetres.
Each millimetre is **one tenth of a centimetre.**

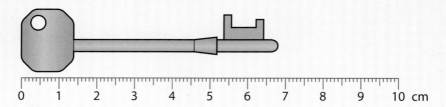

This key is 6 centimetres and 8 millimetres long.
A length of 6 cm and 8 mm is written as 6.8 centimetres or 6.8 cm.

You can write a decimal like 6.47 in different ways to show what it means.

$$6.47 = 6 + 0.4 + 0.07$$
$$= 6 + \frac{4}{10} + \frac{7}{100}$$
$$= 6\frac{47}{100}$$

1 Write in pounds.

   a £2 and 46p   b 40p

   c £5 and 7p   d £20 and 1p

2 Write in pence.

   a £4.27   b £3.06   c £9.20   d £10

3 Write in pounds.

   a 126p   b 82p   c 30p   d 5p

4 Write in metres.

   a 2 m and 46 cm   b 6 m and 9 cm

   c 70 cm   d 5 m and 5 cm

5 Write in centimetres.

   a 5.46 m   b 2.07 m   c 0.3 m   d 0.08 m

6 Write in metres.

   a 354 cm   b 208 cm   c 90 cm   d 6 cm

7 Write in millimetres.

   a 5.4 cm   b 23.1 cm   c 0.7 cm   d 4.0 cm

8 Write in centimetres.

   a 27 mm   b 405 mm   c 3 mm   d 11 mm

9 Write as fractions.

   a 0.71   b 8.13   c 10.09

   d 21.7   e 0.05   f 6.81

10 Write as decimals.

   a $4\frac{19}{100}$ b $12\frac{23}{100}$ c $6\frac{5}{100}$

   d $\frac{73}{100}$ e $2\frac{4}{100}$ f $23\frac{59}{100}$

(11) Copy and complete these.

a $\frac{60}{100} = \frac{\square}{10}$

b $\frac{3}{10} = \frac{\square}{100}$

c $\frac{2}{10} = \frac{20}{\square}$

d $\frac{70}{100} = \frac{7}{\square}$

e $\frac{\square}{100} = \frac{9}{10}$

f $\frac{1}{\square} = \frac{10}{100}$

Points to remember

⊙ 1 whole is equivalent to 10 tenths, or 100 hundredths.

⊙ 1 tenth is equivalent to 10 hundredths.

⊙ 7 tenths is equivalent to 70 hundredths.

6 Percentages of quantities

This lesson will help you to work out percentages.

Exercise 6

Per cent means 'out of 100'.

20 per cent is written as 20%.

20 per cent means 20 out of 100.

This is $\frac{20}{100}$ as a fraction.

50% is the same as $\frac{1}{2}$. To find 50%, find half.

25% is the same as $\frac{1}{4}$. To find 25%, find half of 50%.

10% is the same as $\frac{1}{10}$. To find 10%, divide by 10.

Example 1

Find 5% of £80.

10% of £80 is £80 ÷ 10 = £8.

5% is half of 10%.

So 5% of £80 is £8 ÷ 2 = £4.

Example 2

Find 40% of £90.

10% of £90 is £90 ÷ 10 = £9.

40% is four times 10%.

So 40% of £90 is £9 × 4 = £36.

1 Copy and fill in this table for grids A to F.

	Number of squares shaded	Fraction of grid shaded	Percentage of grid shaded
A			
B			
C			
D			
E			
F			

A 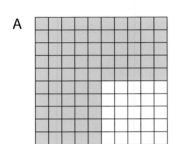 B 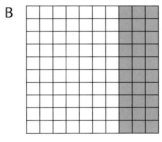 C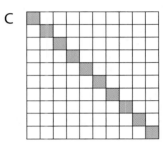

D 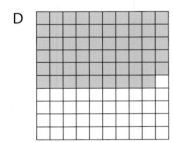 E 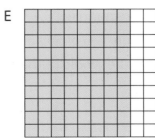 F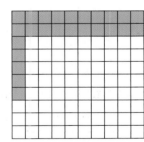

2 What percentage of each shape is shaded?

a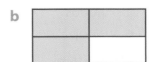

b

c

d

(3) Draw a grid like this one.

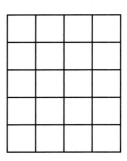

a Colour 10% of the squares red.

b Colour 20% of the squares blue.

c Colour 30% of the squares green.

d What percentage of the squares are not coloured?

e What fraction of the squares are not coloured?

(4) Work these out.

a 50% of £80

b 10% of 70 cm

c 25% of 60 g

d 20% of £300

e 5% of 100 kg

f 75% of 40 km

g 1% of 900 ml

h 2% of 800 g

i 60% of £50

(5) Play **Percentage squares** with a partner.
You need some squared paper and one dice.

Rules

◎ Each of you draws a 5 by 10 rectangle.

◎ Take turns to roll the dice.
Shade that percentage of your rectangle.

For example, if you roll 3, work out 3% of 50 and shade that number of squares.

◎ The winner is the first to shade the whole of their rectangle.

(6) A shop has 200 DVDs for sale.

a 25% of the DVDs are thrillers.
How many of the DVDs are thrillers?

b What percentage of the DVDs are not thrillers?

c 30% of the DVDs are pop videos.
How many of the DVDs are pop videos?

d 20% of the DVDs are comedy films.
How many of the DVDs are comedy films?

e 5% of the DVDs are horror films.
How many of the DVDs are horror films?

f 15% of the DVDs are children's movies.
How many of the DVDs are children's movies?

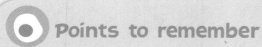

Points to remember

- Per cent means 'in every hundred'. 15% means $\frac{15}{100}$.

- 50% is one half, 25% is one quarter, and 75% is three quarters.

- 10% is one tenth.
  To find 10% of an amount, divide it by 10.

- To find 60%, first find 10%, then multiply by 6.

0%	10%	20%	25%		50%	75%	100%
0	$\frac{1}{10}$	$\frac{1}{5}$	$\frac{1}{4}$		$\frac{1}{2}$	$\frac{3}{4}$	1

How well are you doing?

1 *2002 level 3*

How much of each square grid is shaded?

For each grid, write **More than half** or **Half** or **Less than half**.

a 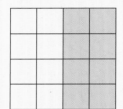   b 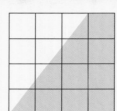   c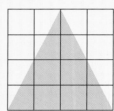

2 *2004 Progress Test level 4*

0.07 is the same as 7 hundredths.

Copy and complete this sentence.

0.7 is the same as 7 ....

3 *2006 Progress Test level 4*

a Half of this square is shaded. What percentage is shaded?

b What percentage of this square is shaded?

(4) *2006 Progress Test level 4*

Copy and complete these.

a $\frac{1}{5}$ of 20 = ☐

b $\frac{3}{4}$ of 20 = ☐

(5) *2003 Progress Test level 4*

Kate is using her computer to print a photo.

The black bar shows how much of the photo is printed so far.

What percentage of the photo is printed so far?

(6) *2003 level 3*

a Here is part of a number line.

What number is the arrow pointing to?

b Work out the answer to 5.3 + 0.9.

(7) *2001 level 4*

Copy and complete these.

a $\frac{2}{12} = \frac{\square}{6}$

b $\frac{1}{2} = \frac{12}{\square}$

c $\frac{1}{\square} = \frac{6}{24}$

(8) *1995 level 4*

Altogether 260 people played different sports at the Sports Centre on Friday.

Copy and complete this table to show how many people played badminton, football and squash on Friday.

Sport	Percentage	Number of people
Badminton	10%	26
Football	40%	...
Squash	5%	...

Length, perimeter and area

This unit will help you to:

- ◉ choose units and equipment to estimate and measure length;
- ◉ measure and draw lines;
- ◉ solve problems involving perimeter and area;
- ◉ work out perimeters and areas by counting, measuring and calculating;
- ◉ know and use the formula for the area of a rectangle.

1 Length

This lesson will help you to estimate, measure and draw lines to the nearest millimetre.

Exercise 1

When you use a ruler to measure a line, put the zero mark of the ruler at the start of the line.

This line is 4.6 cm or 46 mm long.

① Use a ruler to measure these lines.

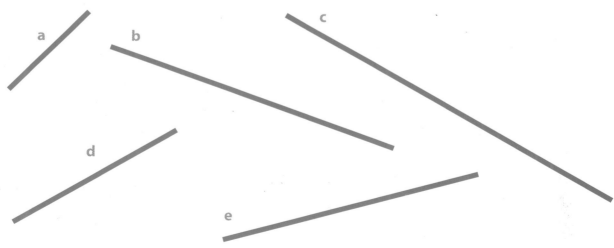

② Use a ruler and sharp pencil to draw lines of these lengths.

a 6 cm   b 9 cm   c 2 cm   d 12 cm   e 14 cm

3 Estimate the length of each line. Write your estimates in your book.

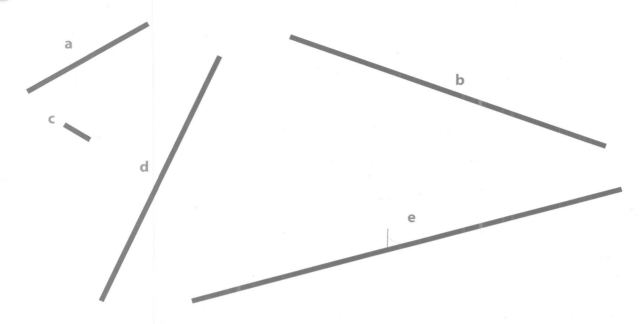

Use a ruler to measure each line accurately.
Write each measurement next to your estimate.

4 Use a ruler and sharp pencil to draw lines of these lengths.
Label each line with its length.

a 4.7 cm   b 9.1 cm   c 12.3 cm   d 0.6 cm   e 10.4 cm

f 18 mm   g 41 mm   h 82 mm   i 35 mm   j 132 mm

5 a Line A is 3 cm 6 mm long.   b Line P is 4 cm 8 mm long.

   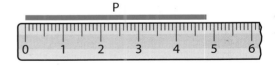

Line B is 7 mm longer than A.   Line Q is 6 mm longer than P.
How long is line B?   How long is line Q?

c Line C is 2 cm 2 mm longer than A.
How long is line C?

d Line R is 2 cm 5 mm shorter than P.
How long is line R?

6 Use a ruler to measure the sides of these rectangles.
For each rectangle, write down the total length of all the sides.

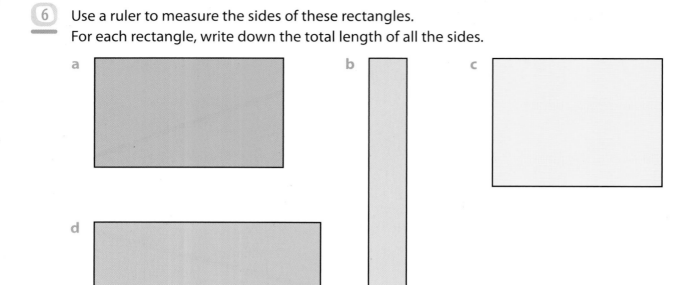

a

b

c

d

7 Use a ruler to measure the sides of these shapes.
For each shape, write down the total length of all the sides.

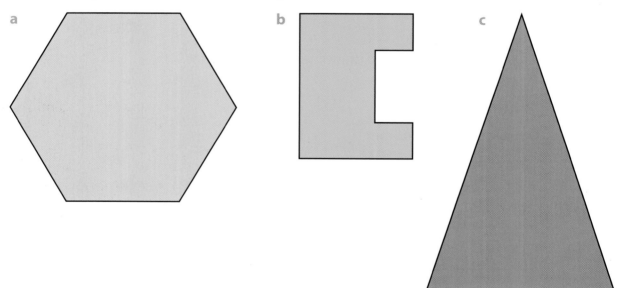

a

b

c

Extension problems

8 The diagram shows part of a ruler.
What is the distance between the two arrows in millimetres?

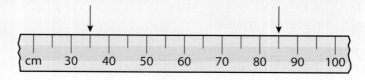

9 Flora and George are measuring different lines to see which is the longest.

Flora says her line is 9.6 cm long.

George says his line is 87 mm long.

Who has measured the longest line?

> ⦿ **Points to remember**
>
> ⊙ When you use a ruler to measure or draw lines, line up the zero mark on the ruler with the beginning of the line.
>
> ⊙ 1 metre is the same as 100 centimetres.
>
> ⊙ 1 centimetre is the same as 10 millimetres.

2 Perimeter

This lesson will help you to measure and calculate perimeters of rectangles and regular polygons.

Exercise 2

Perimeter is the total distance round the edge of a 2D shape.

Example 1

Work out the perimeter of this shape.

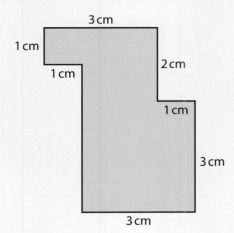

Add up the lengths of all the sides.

$(3 + 2 + 1 + 3 + 3 + 4 + 1 + 1)\,\text{cm}$

$= 18\,\text{cm}$

Example 2

This rectangle is drawn on a centimetre square grid. Work out its perimeter.

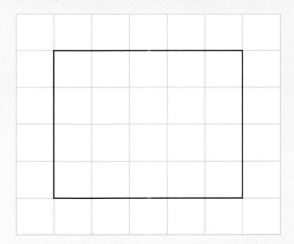

Either add up the lengths of all the sides:

$4\,\text{cm} + 5\,\text{cm} + 4\,\text{cm} + 5\,\text{cm} = 18\,\text{cm}$

or

add the length and width and multiply by 2

$(4\,\text{cm} + 5\,\text{cm}) \times 2 = 18\,\text{cm}$

Example 3

Work out the perimeter of this regular heptagon.

Every side of a regular polygon is the same length.
This is shown by the little marks.

In this case the length of one side is 4 cm.

A heptagon has 7 sides so the perimeter is

$7 \times 4\,\text{cm} = 28\,\text{cm}.$

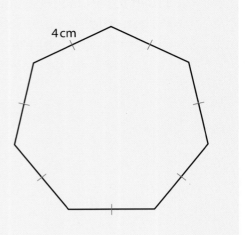

4 cm

---

1   This grid has 1 cm by 1 cm squares.
    Work out the perimeter of each shape.

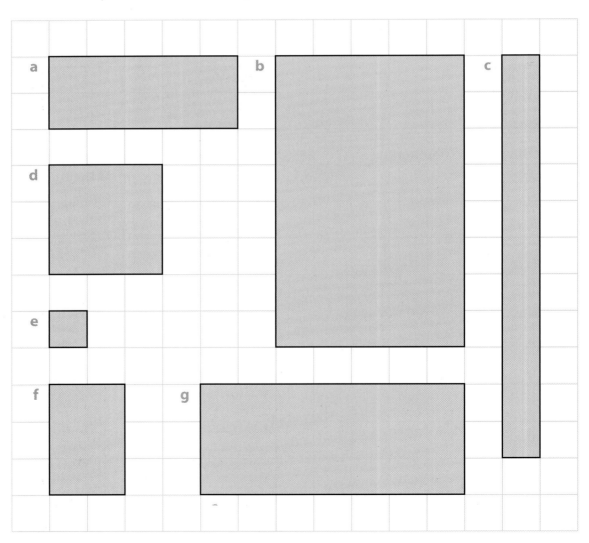

2 Use a ruler to measure the sides of these rectangles.
Then use your measurements to calculate the perimeter of each rectangle.

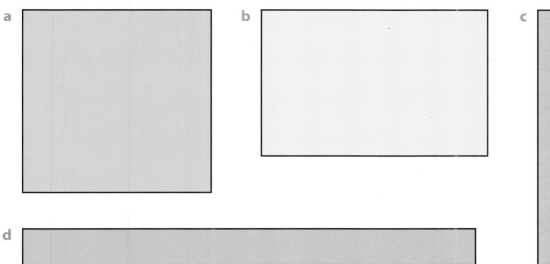

3 This grid has 1 cm by 1 cm squares. Work out the perimeter of each shape.

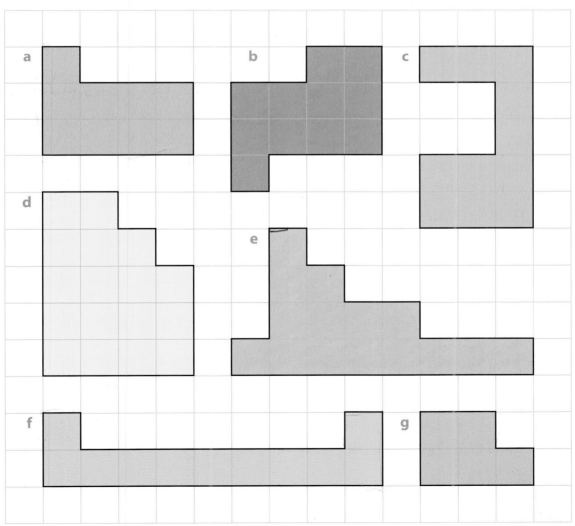

(4) Work out the perimeter of each of these regular shapes.

a
3 cm

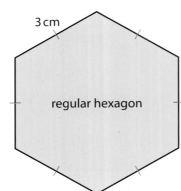

regular hexagon

b
2 cm

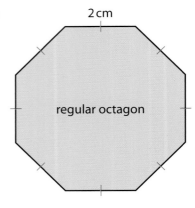

regular octagon

c

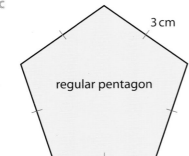

3 cm

regular pentagon

d
1 cm

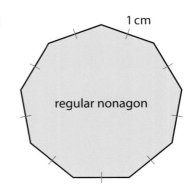

regular nonagon

Extension problems

(5) Andy measures the length and width of a rectangle.
The length is 4.7 cm and the width is 33 mm.
What is the perimeter of the rectangle in millimetres?

(6) One side of a regular pentagon is 9 mm long.
What is the perimeter of the pentagon in centimetres?

⊙ **Points to remember**

- The **perimeter** is the total distance around the edge of a shape.
- Perimeters are measured in units of length such as millimetres, centimetres or metres.
- To find the perimeter of a shape, add up the lengths of all the sides.
- To find the perimeter of a rectangle, add the length and width, then multiply the result by 2.

perimeter of a rectangle = (length + width) × 2

3 Finding areas by counting squares

This lesson will help you to find areas by counting squares.

Area is a measure of surface.

Area is measured in square units such as square centimetres (cm²) or square metres (m²).

Very small areas are often measured in square millimetres (mm²).

Large areas of land are measured in square kilometres (km²).

The UK has an area of 244 820 km².

Example

Find the area of this shape.

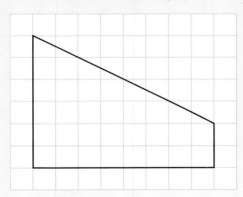

You can find the area by counting the squares.

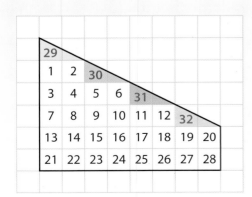

Count the whole squares first. There are 28 whole squares.

Now count the part squares.

Each triangle is half of a rectangle of two squares.
Each triangle has an area of 1 square.
The four triangles have an area of 4 squares.

The total is 32 squares.

You will need some centimetre squared paper and some dotty paper.

1 Work out the area of each of these shapes.
Each square has an area of 1 cm².
Write your answers in square centimetres (cm²).

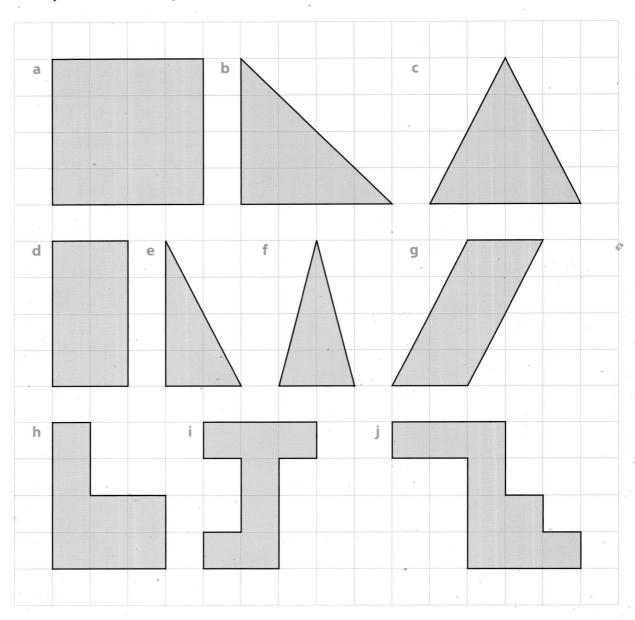

2 On centimetre squared paper draw a rectangle that has an area of 18 cm².
Now draw two more different rectangles with an area of 18 cm².
Which of the three rectangles has the longest perimeter?

3 Copy the triangle carefully onto centimetre squared paper.
Now draw a rectangle with the same area as the triangle.

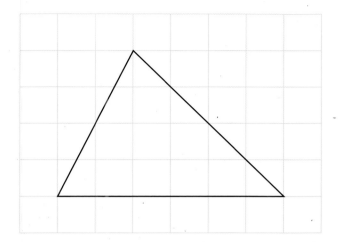

4 Here is a map of an island.

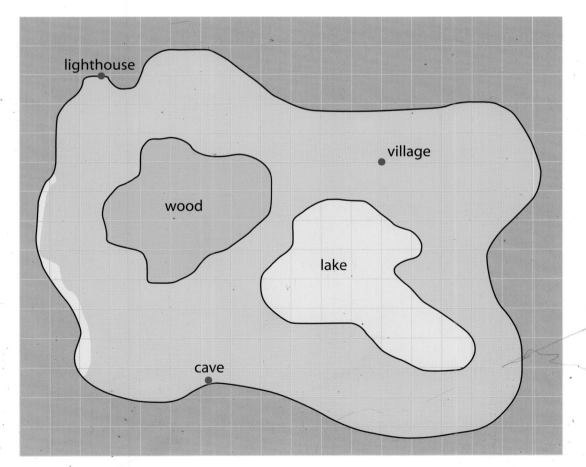

a Estimate the area of the wood in square units.

b Estimate the area of the lake in square units.

c Estimate the area of the island in square units.

5 On centimetre squared paper, draw a 4 by 4 square.

Divide the square into two shapes with equal areas by drawing along the grid lines.

One way to do it is shown on the right.

Do it in as many different ways as possible.

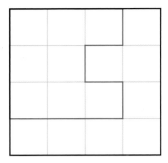

6 You need some dotty paper.
Draw as many different shapes as you can that:

- ⊙ fit on a 3 by 3 dot grid
- ⊙ are made of lines that go from dot to dot
- ⊙ have an area of 2 squares.

One way to do it is shown on the right.

Extension problem

7 Calculate the shaded area of this shape. Each square is 1 cm².

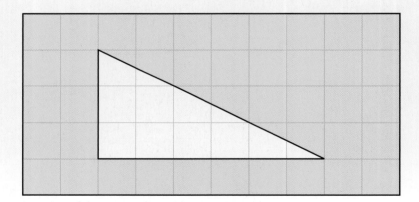

 Points to remember

- ⊙ Area is a measure of the surface covered by a shape.
- ⊙ Area is measured in square units such as cm² and m².
- ⊙ Find the area of a shape by counting the squares that it covers.
- ⊙ Combine part squares to make whole squares.

4 Area of rectangles

This lesson will help you to use the formula 'area of rectangle = length × width' to solve problems.

Exercise 4

You can find areas by counting squares on a grid.
You can also use a formula to calculate areas.

The formula for the area of a rectangle is:

area = length × width

Often, when measurements are shown on a diagram, you are told that it is *not drawn accurately*.
If you see this, do **not** measure the lengths but use the measurements that are given.

Example 1

What is the area of this rectangle?

Area = length × width

Area = 8 × 3 = 24 cm²

Remember that area units must be square units.

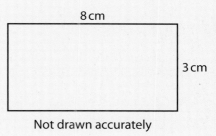

Not drawn accurately

Example 2

Work out the area of this shape.
All the corners are right angles.

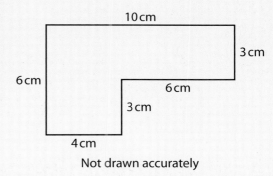

Not drawn accurately

Draw a line across the shape to divide the
shape into two rectangles.

Area = length × width

Area of rectangle 1 = 3 × 10 = 30 cm²

Area of rectangle 2 = 3 × 4 = 12 cm²

Add the two rectangles together to find the
total area.

Total area = 30 + 12 = 42 cm²

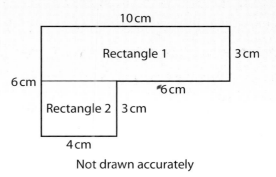

Not drawn accurately

Example 3

The diagram shows two rectangles.
What is the shaded area?

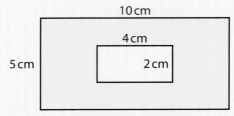

Not drawn accurately

To work out the shaded area, work out the area of the big rectangle.
Subtract the area of the small rectangle.

Area of the big rectangle = $10 \times 5 = 50\,\text{cm}^2$

Area of the small rectangle = $4 \times 2 = 8\,\text{cm}^2$

Shaded area = $50 - 8 = 42\,\text{cm}^2$

1   Work out the area of each of these rectangles and squares.

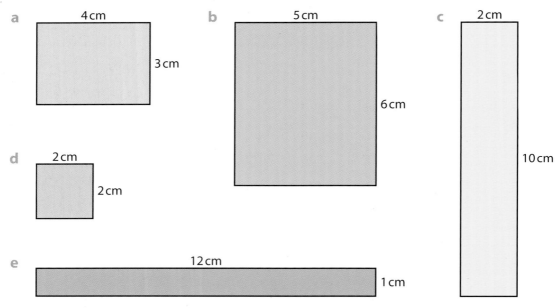

Not drawn accurately

2   A rectangle is 5 cm wide and 8 cm long.
     What is the area of the rectangle?

3   The sides of a square are 10 mm long.
     What is the area of the square?

4 A rectangular football pitch is
55 m wide and 100 m long.
What is its area?

5 Alex has an allotment.
The allotment is in the shape of a rectangle.
The rectangle is 20 m long and 9 m wide.
What is the area of the allotment?

6 A rectangular swimming pool has a perimeter of 28 m.
The length of the pool is 8 m.
Calculate the area of the swimming pool.

Extension problems

7 The L-shape is made from two rectangles. Calculate its area.

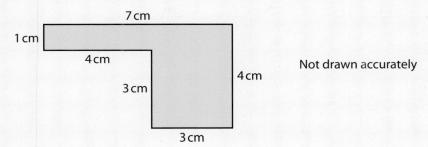

Not drawn accurately

8 The diagram shows two rectangles. Calculate the shaded area in this shape.

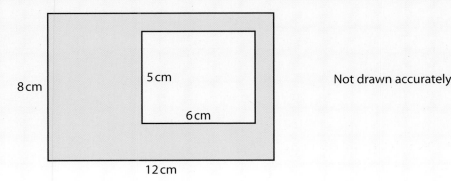

Not drawn accurately

9 A rectangular patio is 450 cm long and 300 cm wide.
The patio is to be tiled.
The tiles are squares of side 50 cm.
How many tiles are needed?

⦿ Points to remember

⊙ Area is a measure of the surface covered by a shape.

⊙ Area is measured in square units such as cm^2 and m^2.

⊙ The formula for the area of a rectangle is:

area of a rectangle = length × width

⊙ The area of a square can be worked out using the same formula.

How well are you doing?

Can you:

- estimate length using mm, cm and m?
- measure and draw lines?
- work out perimeters by measuring, counting and calculating?
- work out areas of rectangles using a formula?

Length, perimeter and area (no calculator)

1 *2003 Progress Test level 3*

Copy and complete each sentence by choosing one of the lengths.

a The length of a banana is about … cm.

2 cm   20 cm   200 cm   2000 cm

b The height of the classroom door is about … cm.

2 cm   20 cm   200 cm   2000 cm

c The width of an exercise book is about … cm.

2 cm   20 cm   200 cm   2000 cm

2 *2004 level 4*

The diagram shows some shapes on a 10 by 6 square grid.

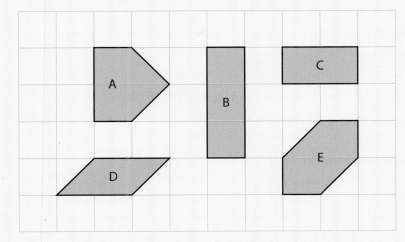

a Which two shapes have the same area as shape A?

b Which two shapes have the same perimeter as shape A?

c How many of shape C would you need to cover a 10 by 6 square grid?

(3) Use a ruler to measure the length of these lines.

a

b

Length, perimeter and area (calculator allowed)

(4) *2004 Paper 2 level 4*

Here is a shaded shape on a centimetre square grid.

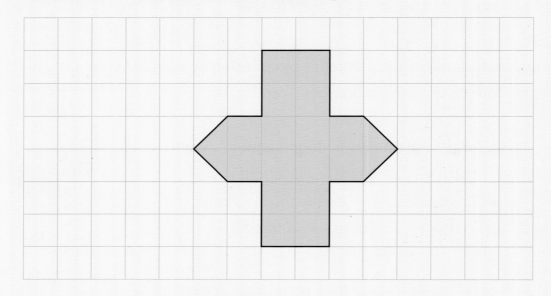

a What is the area of the shaded shape?

b On centimetre square paper draw a rectangle that has the same area as the shaded shape.

(5) A rectangle has a length of 20 m and a width of 14 m.
What is the area of the rectangle?

(6) A rectangle has an area of 40 mm².
The length of the rectangle is 10 mm.

a What is the width of the rectangle?

b What is the perimeter of the rectangle?

Probability 1

This unit will help you to:

- use words and phrases to describe how likely things are to happen;

- know where to place events on a probability scale.

1 Probability scale

This lesson will help you to describe probability and use a probability scale.

 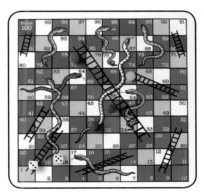 

Exercise 1

Probability is the likelihood or chance of something happening.

For example:

- It is **impossible** that I will see Queen Victoria on my way home from school today.

- It is **likely** that I will have something to eat when I get home from school.

- It is **certain** that 2016 will be a leap year.

Words that describe probability like 'impossible', 'certain', 'likely' or 'unlikely' can be shown on a scale.

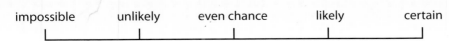

impossible   unlikely   even chance   likely   certain

1. Work in a group of four or five with a set of cards from **S2.2 Resource sheet 1.1**.

   Put the cards in a pile face down on the table.
   Turn the top card over.
   Decide as a group whether the event is **certain**, **possible** or **impossible**.
   Do the same with the other cards in turn and put them into three piles.

   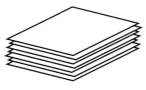 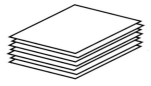 

   Impossible   Possible   Certain

2. Copy and complete these sentences using **certain**, **impossible**, **likely** or **unlikely**.

   a It is .... that it will snow on Christmas Day.

   b It is .... the sun will rise tomorrow.

   c It is .... that I will see a pig flying today.

   d It is .... that I will get homework tonight.

   e It is .... that I will grow taller than my mum.

   f It is .... that I will have my favourite meal tonight.

3. You need a copy of **S2.2 Resource sheet 1.2**.

   a Write the words **impossible**, **certain**, **even chance**, **unlikely** and **likely** in the correct places on the probability scale on the resource sheet.

   b Draw lines connecting the events in the boxes to the correct places on the scale.

⬤ Points to remember

- ⊙ **Probability** is the likelihood or chance of something happening.
- ⊙ Words like 'impossible', 'certain', 'likely', 'unlikely' and 'even chance' describe probability.
- ⊙ Probability can be shown on a probability scale.

impossible   unlikely   even chance   likely   certain

2 Probability experiments

This lesson will help you to place events on a probability scale.

If you flip a coin, there are two possible **outcomes**. You can get a **head** or a **tail**.
There is an **even chance** of getting a head.

It is **likely** that the coin will land flat (but not certain, as it could get stuck somewhere).

It is **impossible** to get a flipped coin to land on its edge.

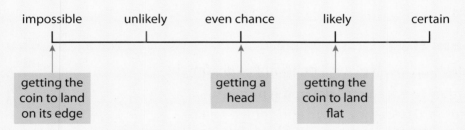

Work with a partner. You will need a dice, a bag containing one blue and three red counters, and a set of 0–9 digit cards.

1 Roll the dice 20 times. One of you should roll the dice and the other write down the scores.

a Write one of these words to describe the probability of each event A to E:

likely, **unlikely**, **even chance**, **certain**, **impossible**

A Scoring a 3

B Scoring a 7

C Scoring an odd number

D Scoring a number from 1 to 6

E Scoring a number bigger than 1

b Copy the probability scale below. Mark events A, B, C, D and E in the right places.

impossible	unlikely	even chance	likely	certain

(2) Put three red counters and one blue counter in the bag.

The first person picks out a counter without looking and puts it back.
The other person writes down its colour.

Do this 10 times, then swap over and repeat.

a   Write one of these words to describe the probability of each event A to D:

   likely, unlikely, even chance, certain, impossible

   A   Picking a red counter

   B   Picking a blue counter

   C   Picking a black counter

   D   Picking a counter of any colour

b   Draw a probability scale like the one in question 1b.
   Mark events A, B, C and D in the right places.

(3) Take a set of digit cards 0–9. Spread out the cards face down and shuffle them.

The first person picks a card without looking.
The other person writes down the number.
Put the card back face down and shuffle again.

Do this 10 times, then swap over and repeat.

a   Write one of these words to describe the probability of each event A to E:

   likely, unlikely, even chance, certain, impossible

   A   Picking the digit 5

   B   Picking any digit from 0 to 9

   C   Picking an odd digit

   D   Picking a digit between 2 and 8

   E   Picking 15

   0 1 2 3 4

   5 6 7 8 9

b   Draw a probability scale like the one in question 1b.
   Mark events A, B, C, D and E in the right places.

Extension problem

 Imagine that you have a eight-sided spinner numbered 1 to 8.

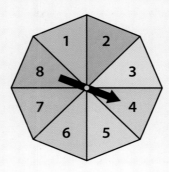

Write down an event for each of these probabilities.

a Certain   b Impossible   c Likely

d Unlikely   e Even chance

◉ Points to remember

⊙ Different events have different chances of happening.

⊙ A probability scale can show how likely or unlikely events are.

impossible	unlikely	even chance	likely	certain

How well are you doing?

Can you:

- tell whether an event is likely, unlikely, certain, impossible or has an even chance of happening?

- use a probability scale to show how likely or unlikely events are?

1 You can spin any number from 1 to 8 on this spinner.
Write a number that it is impossible to get.

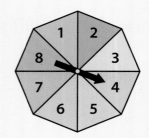

2 Helen has a bag of ten marbles.
4 marbles are blue, 3 are yellow,
2 are pink and 1 is orange.
Helen picks a marble without looking.

Choose a word to describe the likelihood
of each event.

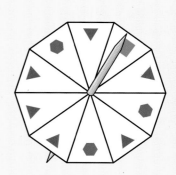

likely, unlikely, even chance, certain, impossible

A Helen picks a red marble.

B She picks a pink marble.

C She picks a blue or yellow marble.

D She picks a pink, yellow, blue or orange marble.

3 Imagine that you have this ten-sided spinner.

Choose a word to describe the likelihood of each event.

certain, most likely, least likely, impossible

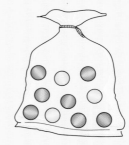

A Spinning a square ■

B Spinning a triangle ▲

C Spinning a hexagon ⬡

Box A

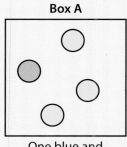

One blue and
three yellow counters

Box B

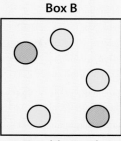

Two blue and
three yellow counters

a I am going to take a counter from one of the boxes without looking.
Which box gives the higher chance of taking a yellow counter?
Explain your answer.

b I am going to take a counter from a different box, box C, without looking.
It is just as likely that I will get a yellow counter as a blue counter.
Draw a picture to show what counters might be in box C.

Where is the mathematics?

This group activity will help you to:

- identify the mathematics in a situation;
- identify mathematical questions to ask about it;
- communicate your findings.

Background

Mathematics is all around us.

Looking for the maths in a situation or in information will help you to understand how widely maths is used.

What mathematical questions could you ask about this picture?

What answers to your questions would you give?

What mathematical questions could you ask about this picture?

What answers to your questions would you give?

Problem 3

What mathematical questions could you ask about this picture?

What answers to your questions would you give?

Be prepared to justify your conclusions to other groups.

Angles

This unit will help you to:

- make and describe clockwise and anticlockwise turns;
- know the number of degrees in a whole, a half and a quarter turn;
- work out angles between compass points and between the hands of a clock;
- measure, estimate and draw acute and obtuse angles.

1 Amounts of turn

This lesson will help you to measure turns and to work out angles on a straight line or around a point.

Exercise 1

The angle of a turn is measured in **degrees** (°).

- A quarter turn is a right angle or 90°.
- A half turn forms a straight line. It is two right angles or 180°.
- A complete turn is four right angles or 360°.

Example 1

Kyra faces north. She turns anticlockwise through a quarter turn.
Which direction is she now facing?

Kyra is now facing west.

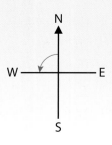

Example 2

What is the angle between the two hands?

There are 90° in a right angle.
At 1 o'clock, the angle between the hands is one third of a right angle.

90° ÷ 3 = 30°

So the angle between the hands at 1 o'clock is 30°.

Example 3

Calculate the missing angle in this diagram.

ADB is a straight line.
Angles on a straight line are two right angles or 180°.

The missing angle is 180° − 25° = 155°.

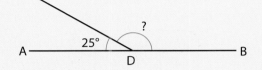

---

1 The map shows five towns and roads between them.

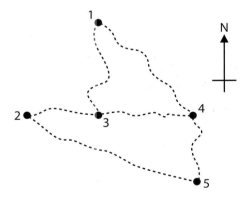

   a A bus drives south from town 1 to town 3.
      It then goes west.
      In which town does the bus end up?

   b In what direction should the bus travel
      to get from town 2 to town 4?

   c The direct road from town 4 to town 1 is closed.
      Write directions to travel from town 4 to town 1.

   d A van driver starts her round in town 5.
      She travels north and then north-west to deliver a parcel.
      In which town does she deliver the parcel?

2 Atul has a sat-nav system in his car.
   Draw a sketch of these instructions.

   Instruction 1: Go north for two miles.
   Instruction 2: Go west for three miles.
   Instruction 3: Go south for two miles.
   Instruction 4: Go east for three miles.

   Where is Atul now?

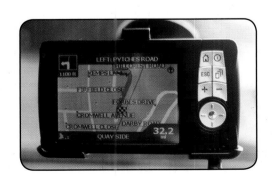

3 A robot is programmed with these instructions.
Draw its path on squared paper.

Instruction 1: Travel south four squares.

Instruction 2: Turn clockwise 90°. Travel forward three squares.

Instruction 3: Turn clockwise 90°. Travel forward four squares.

Instruction 4: Turn clockwise 90°. Travel forward three squares.

What shape has the robot drawn?

4 **a** The time is 6 o'clock.
What is the angle between the hands?

b The time is 3 o'clock.
What is the angle between the hands?

c What is the angle between the clock hands at 11 o'clock?

d What is the angle between the clock hands at 4 o'clock?

5 AB is a straight line. Calculate the size of each angle marked with a letter.

a

60° a

A —————————————— B

b

150° b

A —————————————— B

c

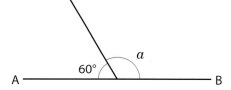
100° c

A —————————————— B

d

20° d

A —————————————— B

6 Calculate the size of each angle marked with a letter.

a

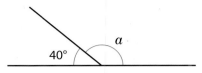

40°   *a*

b

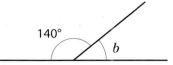

140°   *b*

c

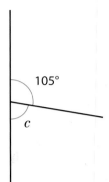

105°

c

d

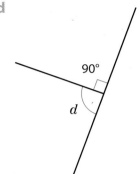

90°

d

e

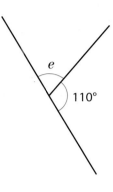

e

110°

Extension problem

7 Calculate the size of each angle marked with a letter.

a

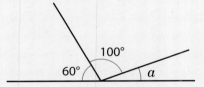

60°   100°   *a*

b

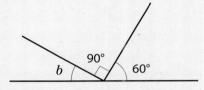

b   90°   60°

c

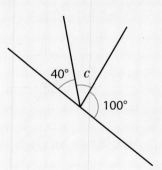

40°   *c*

100°

d

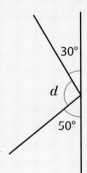

30°

d

50°

2 Measuring angles

This lesson will help you to recognise different types of angles and to measure angles with a protractor.

Did you know that...?

The people in ancient **Mesopotamia** first used 360 degrees for a whole turn 4000 years ago.

No one is sure why they chose 360°. It may be linked to the number of days in a year of their calendar.

The people used to write by scratching marks on clay tablets like the one in the photograph.

Exercise 2

There are three main types of angles.

An **acute angle** is an angle between 0° and 90°.

An **obtuse angle** is an angle between 90° and 180°.

A **reflex angle** is an angle between 180° and 360°.

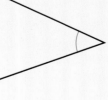

A **protractor** is used to measure the angle between two lines.

The angle in the picture measures 30°.

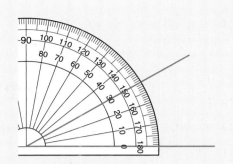

1. Look at these angles.
   For each angle, write whether it is acute, obtuse or reflex.

a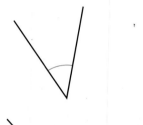

b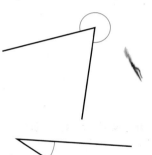

e

c

d

2. Estimate the size of each angle. Record your estimate.
   Measure the angle with a protractor and write its actual size.

a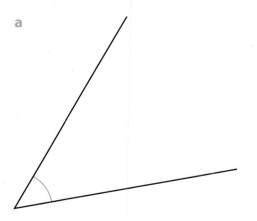

b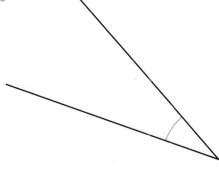

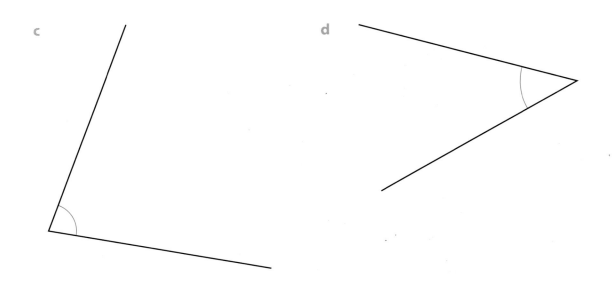

3. Estimate the size of each angle. Record your estimate.
Measure the angle with a protractor and write its actual size.

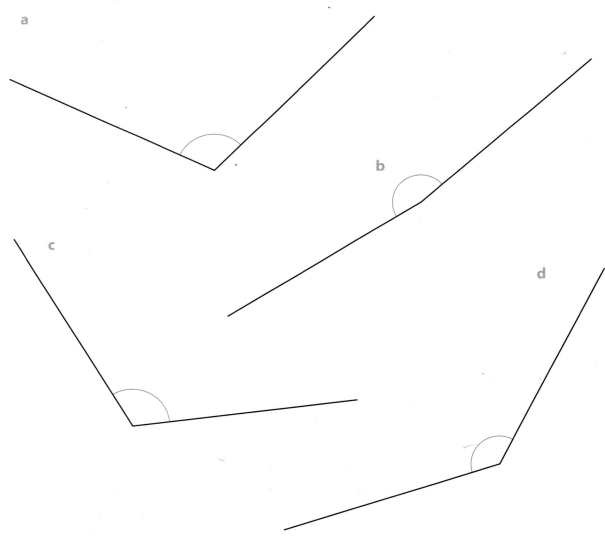

4 Work with a partner on this question.
You will need a set of cards made from **G2.2 Resource sheet 2.1**.

a Estimate the size of each angle to the nearest 10 degrees.

b Arrange the cards in order of size, smallest first. Write the order.

c Measure the size of each angle to the nearest degree.

Extension problems

5 Estimate the size of each of the angles x, y and z.

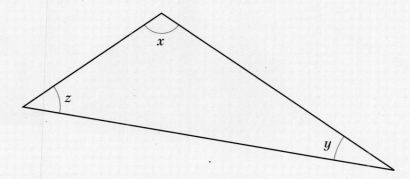

6 Measure each of the angles a, b and c.

Add the three angles together.
What is the answer?

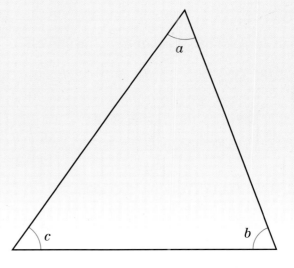

 Points to remember

⊙ Angles can be **acute**, **obtuse** or **reflex**.

⊙ To measure an angle with a **protractor**:
  – line up the baseline along one arm of the angle;
  – put the centre of the baseline where the two arms meet;
  – count up from 0° on the scale to where the second arm crosses the protractor.

3 Drawing angles

This lesson will help you to use a protractor to draw angles.

Exercise 3

Example

Draw an angle of 68° at point A on the line AB.

Line the protractor up with its centre on point A.

Make sure the 0° to 180° baseline of the protractor is on top of the line AB.

Start at 0° and count round until you reach 68°.

Make a mark.

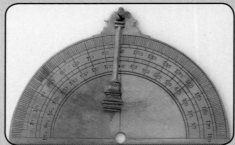

Remove the protractor.

Draw a straight line from the mark to the point A to make the angle.

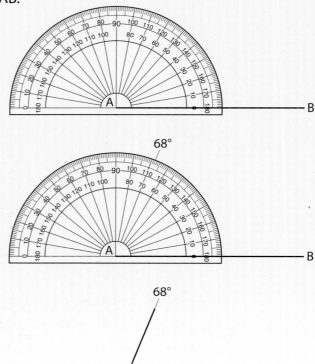

You will need a protractor, ruler and sharp pencil.

1 Draw these acute angles.

    a 20°   b 50°   c 75°   d 40°

2 Draw these obtuse angles.

    a 110°   b 160°   c 95°   d 135°

3 Make an accurate drawing of each triangle.

a

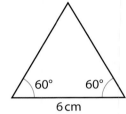

b

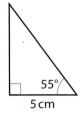

Extension problem

4 Make an accurate drawing of this triangle.

Measure the acute angle at C.

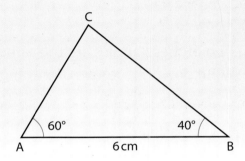

Points to remember

⊙ An **acute angle** lies between 0° and 90°.
An **obtuse angle** lies between 90° and 180°.
A **reflex angle** lies between 180° and 360°.

⊙ To draw an angle using a **protractor and ruler**:
  – draw a line to be one arm of the angle;
  – place the baseline along this line so the centre lies at the point where
    you want to draw the angle;
  – count up from 0° on the scale to the angle you want to draw, then
    make a small mark;
  – use a ruler to draw a straight line from the point to the mark.

How well are you doing?

Angles

You need a ruler, protractor and sharp pencil.

1 *1998 level 3*

    a Two of these angles are the same size.
       Write down the letters of the angles that are the same size.

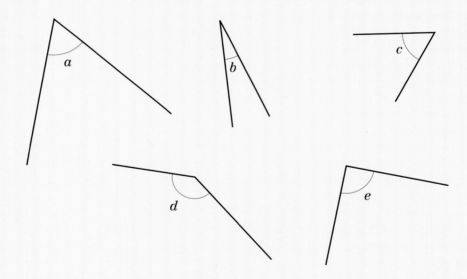

    b Draw an angle which is bigger than a right angle.

c Kelly is facing north.
  She turns anticlockwise through 2 right angles.
  Which direction is she facing now?

d Aled is facing west.
  He turns clockwise through 3 right angles.
  Which direction is he facing now?

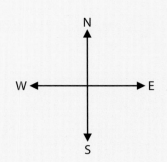

2 *2004 Progress Test level 4*

a Look at these angles.

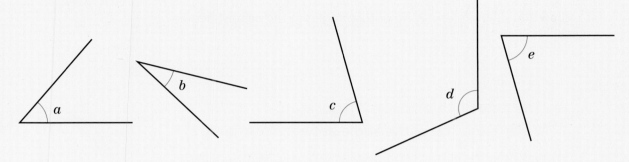

  Write the letter of the smallest angle.

b Now look at these angles.
  They are drawn on a square grid.

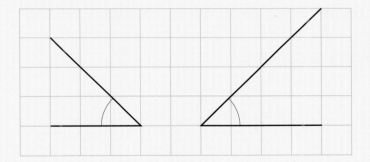

  Ali says the angles are not the same size.
  Is he correct? Write **Yes** or **No**.
  Explain your answer.

3 Measure these angles.

a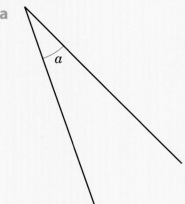

b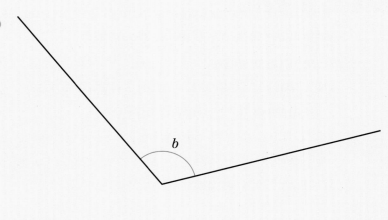

4 *1999 level 4*

   a The time on this clock is 3 o'clock.
What is the size of the angle between the hands?

   b What is the size of the angle between the hands
at 1 o'clock?

   c What is the size of the angle between the hands
at 5 o'clock?

5 Draw accurately an angle of 55 degrees. Label your angle.

6 Work out the size of angle *a*.

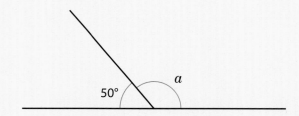

Decimals

This unit will help you to:

- order and round decimals and place them on a number line;
- add and subtract decimals;
- change metres to centimetres, and pounds to pence, and vice versa;
- use a calculator to solve money and other word problems.

1 Decimals and the number line

This lesson will help you to identify decimals on a number line.

Did you know that...?

Americans use a dot to separate the whole number from the tenths in a decimal like 4.6. But not everyone does this.

- In the UK we used to write a raised dot like this: **4·6**
- In the Middle Ages people put a bar over the units digit like this: **4̄6**
- In some European countries a comma is used like this: **4,6**
- In Arabic a forward slash / is used instead of the dot.

Exercise 1

Here is the number line from 6 to 7. It is labelled in tenths.

The arrow is pointing to a number between 6.3 and 6.4.

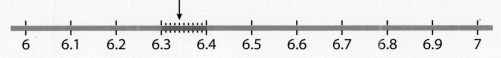

Zooming in on the red section of the line between 6.3 and 6.4 shows the hundredths. The arrow is pointing to 6.34.

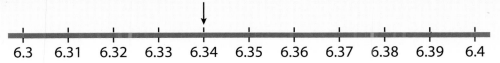

1. Write the value of the **4** in each number.

   a 28.43   b 4138.5   c 1.243   d 346.7   e 0.814

2. Write the number that each arrow is pointing to.

   a

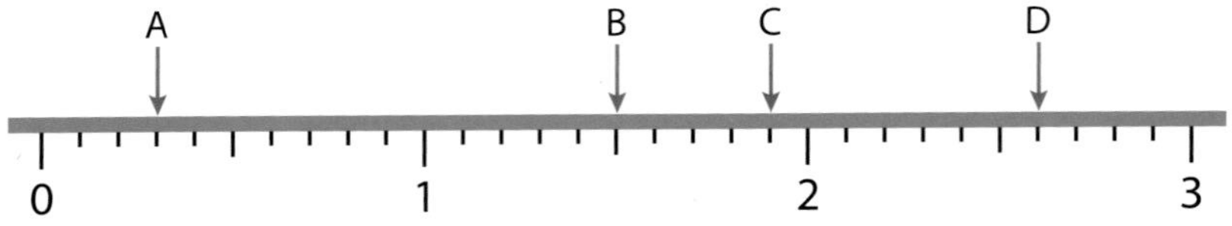

   b

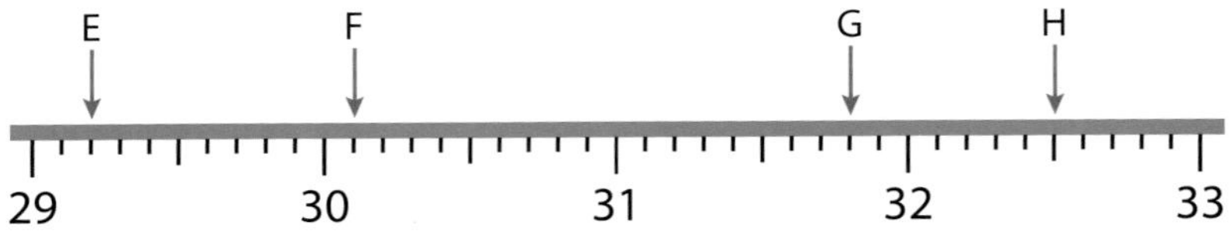

3. Write the number that each arrow is pointing to.

   a

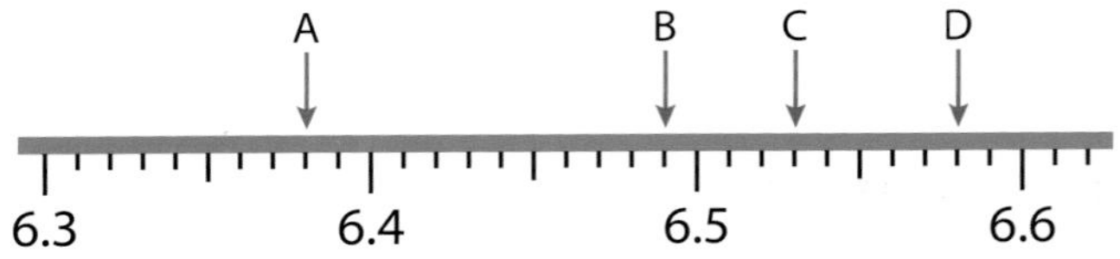

   b

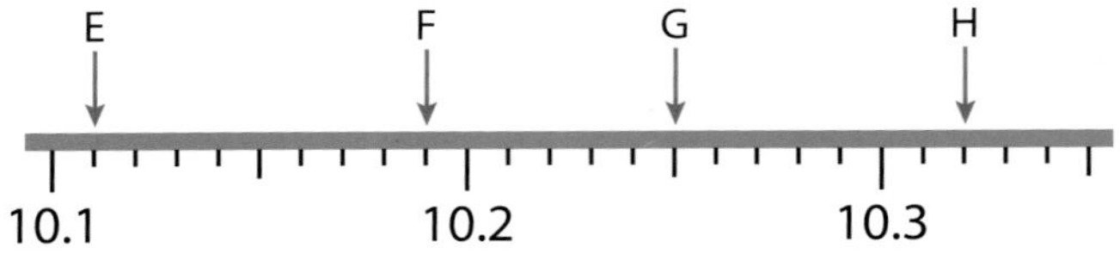

   c

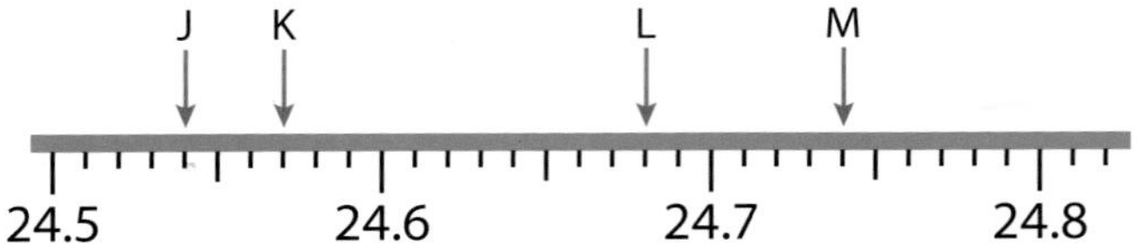

   d

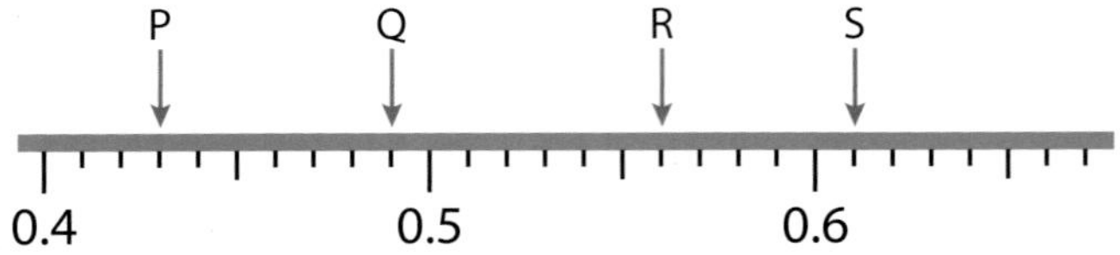

4 **What are these numbers?**

   a One tenth more than 8.3   b Four tenths less than 7.5

   c Five tenths more than 6.7   d Three tenths less than 9.1

   e One hundredth more than 5.6   f Five hundredths less than 7.8

   g Three hundredths more than 1.29   h Four hundredths less than 5.72

5 **Write the next four terms in each sequence.**
Use the number line to help you.

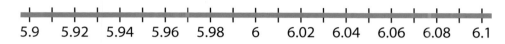

   a 5.94   5.96   5.98   6   …   …   …   …

   b 5.9   5.93   5.96   5.99   …   …   …   …

6 a Jill's height is between 1.3 and 1.4 metres.
     Write a possible height for Jill in metres.

   b Bashir jumped between 4.28 and 4.29 metres.
     Write a possible length for Bashir's jump in metres.

   c A jug holds between 1.9 and 2 litres of water.
     Write a possible amount in litres for the water in the jug.

7 **Estimate the numbers that the arrows are pointing to.**

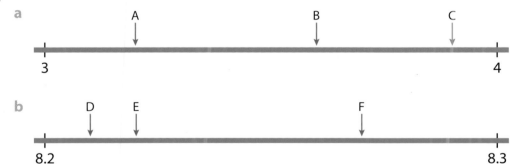

2 Ordering decimals

This lesson will help you to put a set of decimals in order.

The columns show the values of the digits in five numbers:

   7.53,   7.5,   7.6,   7.65,   7.56

To order the numbers, look first at the units.

All the numbers have 7 units, so look at the tenths.

7.6 and 7.65 both have 6 tenths.
7.65 has 5 hundredths so 7.65 is bigger than 7.60.

7.53, 7.50 and 7.56 all have 5 tenths.
To order these, use the hundredths.

Starting with the biggest, the order of the five numbers is:

   7.65,   7.6,   7.56,   7.53,   7.5

units		tenths	hundredths
7	.	5	3
7	.	5	0
7	.	6	0
7	.	6	5
7	.	5	6

1   Write each set of numbers in order of size.
Start with the smallest number each time.

a

units		tenths	hundredths
5	.	7	7
5	.	0	7
5	.	7	

b

tens	units		tenths	hundredths	thousandths
6	8	.	3	8	3
6	8	.	3	8	7
6	8	.	3	7	

2   Look at these amounts of money.

   £70.07   £7.77   £70.70   £7.70   £77.00   £7.07

Write them in order. Start with the smallest amount.

3   Look at this list of numbers.

   0.5   0.8   0.23   0.09   0.67

Write all the numbers in the list that are bigger than 0.6.

4 Write each set of numbers in order of size.
Start with the smallest.

a 5.76   5.66   5.67

b 2.11   2   2.1   2.01

c 0.04   0.4   0.42   0.2

d 13.24   13.2   13.42   13.4

5 This table shows the heights of five children.

Child	Height (m)
Lucy	1.34
Andrew	1.4
Chris	1.43
Ian	1.33
Debbie	1.3

Write the names in order of the children's heights. Start with the tallest.

6 The table shows the time, in seconds, in which five runners ran 100 m.

Runner	Time (s)
Linford	10.2
Dwain	10.02
Roger	10.23
Colin	10.12
Morris	10.21

Write the order in which the runners finished.

7 Write the next four terms in each sequence.
Use the number line to help you.

7.9   7.92   7.94   7.96   7.98   8   8.02   8.04   8.06   8.08   8.1

a 7.96   7.99   8.02   …   …   …   …

b 7.91   7.95   7.99   …   …   …   …

c 7.9   7.95   8   …   …   …   …

(8) Play **Get in order** with a partner. You need two dice.

Rules

◉ Each player should draw a strip of six boxes like this.

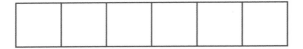

◉ Take turns to roll the dice.

◉ Make a decimal with the dice.
If you roll 6 and 4 you can make 6.4 or 4.6.

◉ Write the decimal in one of the boxes on your strip.

◉ The numbers in the boxes must be in order.
The smallest number must be on the left and the biggest on the right.

◉ If you can't write the decimal in one of the boxes, miss that turn.

◉ The winner is the first player to fill their strip with decimals in order, or the player who has written most decimals on their strip when time is up.

(9) Write each set of numbers in order of size.
Start with the smallest.

a   2.31   2.41   2.134   2.34   2.13

b   0.373   0.37   0.73   0.33   0.733

c   8.038   8.308   8.3   8.83   8.803

d   0.045   0.05   0.504   0.055   0.405

⦿ **Points to remember**

⊙ To compare the size of decimals, it can help to write them in columns.

⊙ Work from the left.
First compare the whole-number parts.
After that, compare the tenths,
then the hundredths,
then the thousandths.

3 Rounding

This lesson will help you to round decimals to the nearest whole number.

Exercise 3

If they have too many decimal places, decimals can be rounded.

Example 1

Round 6.3 to the nearest whole number.

6.3 is between 6 and 7.
6.3 is closer to 6 than 7.
6.3 rounded to the nearest whole number is 6.

Example 2

Round 6.8 to the nearest whole number.

6.8 is closer to 7 than 6.
6.8 rounded to the nearest whole number is 7.

Example 3

Round 6.5 to the nearest whole number.

6.5 is halfway between 6 and 7.
If a number is exactly halfway between two numbers,
the rule is to round up.
6.5 rounds to 7.

To round a number without using a number line, look at the tenths digit.
If the tenths digit is less than 5, don't change the whole-number part.
If the tenths digit is 5 or more, add 1 to the whole-number part.

It is often useful to work out an estimate to an answer. Estimates can be worked out by rounding the numbers in the calculation.

Example 4

Estimate:

a 6.7×3.1

b the total cost of 5 CDs at £8.99 each.

a 6.7×3.1
6.7 rounds to 7 and 3.1 rounds to 3.
$7 \times 3 = 21$ so an estimate is 21.

b £8.99 $\times$ 5
£8.99 rounds to £9.
$£9 \times 5 = £45$ so an estimate for the total cost is £45.

1. Round these to the nearest whole number.

    a 4.8
    b 7.2
    c 12.5
    d 19.9
    e 0.6
    f 2.67
    g 3.08
    h 25.29

2. Round these to the nearest pound.

    a £4.95
    b £45.56
    c £17.09
    d £100.04
    e £8.99
    f £124.25
    g £2.50
    h £19.99

3. Round these to the nearest metre.

    a 8.7 m
    b 9.48 m
    c 0.76 m
    d 3.09 m

4. Round these to the nearest kilogram.

    a 3.14 kg
    b 3.199 kg
    c 8.499 kg
    d 99.9 kg

5. Round these to the nearest litre.

    a 0.8 litre
    b 2.15 litres
    c 39.95 litres
    d 4.5 litres

6. Estimate the answers.

    a $1.8 + 8.2$
    b $11.1 - 3.5$
    c 4.6×3.2
    d $12.3 \div 3.9$

7. Estimate the cost of:

    a four magazines at £1.89 each

    b three newspapers at £1.37 each

    c six paperbacks at £3.99 each

    d nine rolls of paper at £0.98 each

    e two CDs at £9.14 each

    f five games at £12.25 each.

8. Estimate the total cost of:

    a three bottles of shampoo at £1.23 each and two bars of soap at £0.89 each

    b six pineapples at £2.17 each and twelve oranges at 95p for four

    c four chickens at £5.17 each and three lamb chops at £1.65 each.

9. Sam buys three pens at £1.99 each, four postcards at £0.86 each
   and one packet of envelopes at £2.87.
   Estimate how much change he will get from £20.

10 Jenna wants to buy three CDs that cost £9.87 each. She has £30.
Does she have enough money to buy the three CDs?
Give a reason for your answer.

 Points to remember

⊙ To round a decimal to the nearest whole number, look at the tenths digit.
If it is 5 or more, round up.
If it is less than 5, round down.
⊙ You can estimate results of calculations by using rounding.
For example, 4.8×6.2 is about $5 \times 6 = 30$.

4 Decimals and money

This lesson will help you to change pounds to pence, and vice versa, and to use a calculator to solve money problems.

ⓘ **Did you know that...?**

The UK and the Irish Republic changed to a decimal system of pounds and pence on **Decimal Day, 15 February 1971**.

The old money was pounds, shillings and pence. There were 4 farthings in one penny, 12 pence in one shilling and 20 shillings in £1.

Some people called a sixpence a 'tanner' and a shilling a 'bob'.

Russia was the first country in the world to have a **decimal currency**.
In 1710, Peter the Great set the ruble equal to 100 kopecks.

Exercise 4

When you solve a problem involving money, you must change all the amounts to pounds, or change them all to pence.

£1.43 is the same as 143p

98p is the same as £0.98

90p is the same as £0.90

8p is the same as £0.08

Remember to include the £ or p sign in your answer.

Example

Mandy buys a magazine costing £2.65 and a book costing £4.95.
She pays with a £10 note.
How much change should Mandy get?

Estimate the answer:

Magazine: £3   Book: £5   Total: £8   Change from £10: £2

Use your calculator to work out 2.65 + 4.95

②.⑥⑤⊕④.⑨⑤⊜

The display shows [7.6] which means £7.60

Work out 10 − 7.6 to find the change.

①⓪⊖⑦.⑥⊜

The display shows [2.4] which means £2.40

So Mandy should get £2.40 change.

---

1   Write these in pounds.

   a   328p   b   65p   c   20p   d   7p

2   a   Three lunches cost £12.81.
       What does one lunch cost?

   b   Three desserts cost £6.06.
       What does one dessert cost?

   c   What is the cost of one lunch and
       one dessert?

   d   What would be the total cost of
       two lunches and four desserts?

3   Suzy has saved £480 for her new kitchen.

   She wants a fridge costing £128.72,
   a freezer costing £153.85
   and a cooker costing £286.33.

   How much more does she need to save?

Work on questions 4 and 5 with a partner.

(4) Here is the menu at Carlo's Café

Patrick had a meal at Carlo's Café.
His meal cost £3.34.
He had one item from each menu section.
What four items did Patrick choose?

(5) You are going with five friends for a meal at
Carlo's Café. You are paying!

You have £17 to spend.

These are the rules.

- Everyone must have the same meal.

- Everyone must have at least one item
  from each of the four menu sections.

- The total must be less than £17.

What are you going to choose?

(6) Play **Stamp cards** with a partner.
You need one dice and two calculators.

Each player should draw a stamp card like this.

55p	18p	43p
26p	38p	34p

Rules

- Take turns to roll the dice.

- Choose a stamp on your card. Use your calculator to work out your score by
  multiplying the stamp value by the dice number. For example, if you
  roll 5 and choose the 26p stamp, your score is 26p × 5 = 130p = £1.30.

- Write your score in the space on your card.
  Each space can be used only once.

- When all the spaces are full, work out the total amount on your card.

- The winner is the player with the highest amount.

Carlo's Cafe
Menu

Hamburger	£1.20
Cheeseburger	£1.50
Veggieburger	£1.10
Fries	65p
Baked potato	85p
Cookies	15p
Ice cream	50p
Apple pie	99p
Large soda pop	99p
Small soda pop	49p
Milkshake	£1.20

Extension problems

7 The table shows the cost of coach tickets to different cities.

		Liverpool	Blackpool	Chester
Adult	single	£12.50	£15.60	£10.25
	return	£23.75	£28.50	£19.30
Child	single	£8.50	£10.80	£8.25
	return	£14.90	£17.90	£14.70

a What is the total cost for a return journey to Blackpool for one adult and two children?

b How much more does it cost for two adults to make a single journey to Liverpool than to Chester?

8 a 2753 people go to a basketball match.
Each person pays £2.30 for a ticket.
What is the total amount of ticket money collected?

b Programmes cost 65p each.
The total money from programme sales is £612.95.
How many programmes are sold?

Points to remember

- In a money context, 3.6 in a calculator display means £3.60.
- Change all amounts to pounds before you add or subtract them.
- In the answer to a money problem, include the £ sign (if it is in pounds) or p (if it is in pence), but not both.
- To show your working, write the calculation in full with the answer.

5 Adding and subtracting decimals

This lesson will help you to change metres to centimetres and add and subtract decimals.

Exercise 5

An empty number line can help you to do mental calculations.

Example 1   2.7 + 5.4

Count on 5.4 from 2.7.

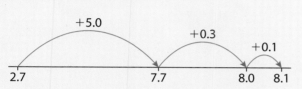

Answer: 8.1

Example 2   9.4 − 5.8

Count up from 5.8 to 9.4.

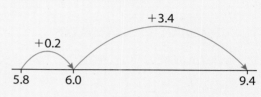

Answer: 0.2 + 3.4 = 3.6

When you add or subtract decimals by writing them in columns, line up the decimal points under each other, tenths under tenths, and so on. Use rounding to estimate the answer.

You can fill empty places at the end of the number with **0** so that the numbers have the same number of decimal places.

Example 3   52.69 + 43.7

Estimate: 53 + 44 = 97

```
    52.69
  + 43.70
    96.39
      1
```

Answer: 96.39

Example 4   6.2 − 1.57

Estimate: 6 − 2 = 4

```
     6.20
   − 1.57
     0.43   to make 2.00
     4.20   to make 6.20
     4.63
```

Answer: 4.63

Do this exercise **without using a calculator**. Show your working.

1 Work these out.

   a 6.88 + 1.32   b 20.4 − 4.8   c 13.1 + 5.69

   d 36.27 − 18.3   e 5.2 + 6.175 + 12.46   f 20.5 − 3.86

2 Anne buys a packet of biscuits at 78p, a packet of crisps at 35p,
three bottles of water at 43p each and a ready meal at £4.56.
She pays with a £20 note.
How much change should she get?

③ Two teams took part in a relay race.
The times in seconds for each runner
are shown in the tables below.

Team A	Time (s)
Runner 1	10.54
Runner 2	10.2
Runner 3	10.11
Runner 4	9.87

Team A	Time (s)
Runner 1	10.6
Runner 2	10.27
Runner 3	9.98
Runner 4	9.89

Which team won? Explain your answer.

④ Write these in centimetres.
a 8.27 m   b 3.06 m   c 0.8 m   d 0.03 m

⑤ Write these in metres.
a 4285 cm   b 300 cm   c 60 cm   d 1 cm

⑥ Write these in millimetres.
a 8.6 cm   b 50.2 cm   c 0.4 cm   d 3.0 cm

⑦ Write these in centimetres.
a 55 mm   b 2085 mm   c 7 mm   d 15 mm

⑧ A plank of wood is 4.5 m long.
Ben cuts off 1.85 m from the plank of wood.
How long is the piece of wood that is left?

⑨ James is 1.9 m tall.
Sarah is 1.52 m tall.
How many centimetres taller than Sarah is James?

⑩ The top of a coffee table is 1.4 m long and 85 cm wide.
How long is the perimeter of the table top?

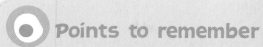

Points to remember

- You can use jottings to help you to do mental calculations.
- To add or subtract decimals in columns, line up the decimal points, put tenths under tenths, and so on.
- Change measurements to the same units before you add or subtract them.

6 Using a calculator

This lesson will help you to develop your calculator skills and use a calculator in different contexts.

Exercise 6

When you use a calculator, you need to decide what calculations to do and make sense of the calculator display.

Example 1

A box holds 25 exercise books.
How many boxes are needed to hold 1450 exercise books?

To solve this, you need to use division. The calculation is 1450 ÷ 25.

An estimate of the answer is 1500 ÷ 30 = 50.

Key in: ⑴⑷⑸⓪÷⑵⑸⊜

The calculator displays ⬛ 58 , close to the estimate.
Answer: 58 boxes.

Example 2

A can of cola costs 46p. A sandwich costs £1.28.
Work out the total cost of 15 cans of cola and 22 sandwiches.

Use multiplication to work out the total cost of the sandwiches.
Then use multiplication to work out the total cost of the cola.
Add the two amounts to find the total cost.

The sandwiches cost 1.28 × 22   ⑴．⑵⑻×⑵⑵⊜
Answer: £28.16

The cans of cola cost 0.46 × 15   ⓪．⑷⑹×⑴⑸⊜
Answer: £6.90

The total cost is £28.16 + £6.90   ⑵⑻．⑴⑹＋⑹．⑼⓪⊜
Answer: £35.06

Use your calculator to solve these problems.

1 Mary gets paid £6.85 for each hour that she plants bulbs.
How much is she paid for 12 hours of work?

2 An ice lolly costs 45p.
How many lollies can you buy for £18?

3 Harry works for 35 hours.
He is paid £219.80.
How much does Harry earn in one hour?

4 Chris wants to make 5 wooden shelves.
Each shelf is to be 76 centimetres long.
How many metres of wood should Chris buy?

5 There are 2.5 metres of sticky tape on a full roll.
Lara uses 72 centimetres of the tape from a full roll.
How much tape is left on the roll?

6 6 adults and 4 children visit a museum.
Each adult pays £4.10 and each child pays £2.40.
How much change do they get from £40?

7 To make a paper clip you need 6.25 cm of wire.
How many paper clips can you make with 1 metre of wire?

8 A tin of paint costs £8.35.
A paint brush costs £4.25.
Find the total cost of 8 tins of paint and 2 paint brushes.

9 A large tin of paint holds $4\frac{1}{2}$ litres.
John needs 27 litres of paint to paint his house.
How many tins of paint should he buy?

10 A bar of chocolate costs 85p.
Ibrahim has a £10 note.

    a How many bars of chocolate can he buy?

    b How much change will he get?

Extension problems

11 A drink and a box of popcorn together cost 90p.
Two drinks and a box of popcorn together cost £1.45.
What does a box of popcorn cost?
Explain how you worked out your answer.

12 12 904 people go to a football match.
The football ground takes £100 006 for the seats.
What is the price of one seat?

> ### ⦿ Points to remember
>
> ⦿ When you use your calculator, write down the calculation that you do.
> It may get you a mark even if you make a mistake.
>
> ⦿ If you make a mistake entering a calculation, clear the display and
> start again.
>
> ⦿ Always estimate the answer and check your answer against the
> estimate.

How well are you doing?

Can you:

- put decimals in order and place them on a number line?
- round decimals to the nearest whole number?
- add and subtract decimals?
- change metres to centimetres, and pounds to pence, and vice versa?
- solve money and other word problems?
- use a calculator in different contexts?

Decimals (no calculator)

1 *2005 level 3*

   a Write a number bigger than one thousand but smaller than one thousand one hundred.
   Write the number in figures not words.

   b Now write a decimal number bigger than zero but smaller than one.

2 *2003 KS2 level 4*
Calculate 8.52 − 7.78.

3 *2004 KS2 level 4*

   a A shop sells three types of sunglasses.

   What is the difference in price between the most expensive and least expensive sunglasses?

£4.69

£2.99

£5.85

£3.29 each

   b The shop also sells sun hats.

   Ryan buys the £4.69 sunglasses and a sun hat.

   How much change does he get from £10?

Decimals (calculator allowed)

4 *2001 KS2 level 4*

What is the missing number on this number line?

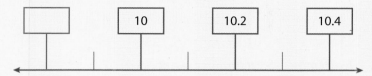

5 *2006 level 4*

The pupils in a class had a sponsored swim.
They collected £429.24.

a How much is £429.24 to the nearest hundred pounds?

b How much is £429.24 to the nearest ten pounds?

6 *2004 Progress Test level 4*

Three pupils answered different questions.
This is what each pupil's calculator showed:

a Asim's question was about money.
Copy and complete the sentence:

3.5 means £3 and … pence.

b Ben's question was about time.
Copy and complete the sentence:

3.5 means 3 hours and … minutes.

c Charlie's question was about length.
Copy and complete the sentence:

3.5 means 3 metres and … centimetres.

7 *1995 KS2 level 4*

a On sports day children get points for
how far they jump.

Joe jumped 138 cm.
How many points does he get?

b Sam said: 'I jumped 1.5 metres. I get 4 points.'
Give a reason why Sam is correct.

Standing Long Jump		
Over	80 cm	1 point
Over	100 cm	2 points
Over	120 cm	3 points
Over	140 cm	4 points
Over	160 cm	5 points
Over	180 cm	6 points

Sequences, functions and graphs

This unit will help you to:

- learn more about number sequences;
- know what a function machine is;
- find inputs, outputs and rules for function machines;
- record inputs and outputs of function machines in tables, as mapping diagrams and as graphs.

1 Sequences

This lesson will remind you how to generate and describe number sequences.

Did you know that...?

Pythagoras lived in Greece around 500 BC.

He liked to study numbers.

He thought that each number had its own personality.

He felt that some numbers were beautiful, some ugly, some masculine and others feminine.

Pythagoras was also keen on music.

Exercise 1

A **sequence** of numbers follows a rule. The sequence

$$3, \quad 8, \quad 13, \quad 18, \quad 23, \quad \ldots$$

follows the rule 'add 5'. The next term is 28.

You can make a sequence if you know the first term and the rule.

Example 1

The first term of a sequence is 7. The rule is 'add 2'.
Write the first five terms of the sequence.

The sequence is 7, 9, 11, 13, 15, …

Example 2

Look at this sequence:

1, ☐, ☐, ☐, 13

Work out the term-to-term rule. Complete the sequence.

There are four steps from 1 to 13. Each step is 12 ÷ 4 = 3. The rule is 'add 3'.

The sequence is 1, 4, 7, 10, 13.

---

1 Look at this sequence.

6,   13,   20,   27,   34,   …

  a What is the 4th term?

  b What is the difference between the 2nd term and the 3rd term?

  c Write the next three terms of the sequence.

2 For each sequence, write the rule and the next three terms.

  a 2,   6,   10,   14,   18,   …,   …,   …

  b 5,   8,   11,   14,   17,   …,   …,   …

  c 50,   48,   46,   44,   42,   …,   …,   …

  d 75,   70,   65,   60,   55,   …,   …,   …

  e 3,   13,   23,   33,   43,   …,   …,   …

  f 7,   16,   25,   34,   43,   …,   …,   …

3 Write the next five terms of each of these sequences.

	1st term	Term-to-term rule
a	1	add 4
b	5	add 8
c	88	subtract 3
d	75	subtract 7
e	2	add 15

4 Copy and complete each sequence.

a 1,   4,   7,   10,   ☐,   ☐,   19

b ☐,   ☐,   8,   10,   12,   14,   ☐

c 5,   ☐,   ☐,   20,   25,   ☐,   35

d 100,   97,   ☐,   ☐,   88,   85,   ☐

e 80,   ☐,   ☐,   65,   60,   55,   ☐

f ☐,   ☐,   27,   ☐,   45,   54,   63

5 Play **Spot the number** with a partner.

Rules

⊙ Each of you choose a number from 1 to 30.
Don't tell your partner what it is.

⊙ Look at the statements below.

A it is even	**B** it is odd	**C** it is square
D it has 1 digit	**E** it has 2 digits	**F** it is a multiple of 3
G it is a multiple of 6	**H** its units digit is 3	**I** its tens digit is 2
J it is less than 20	**K** it is more than 30	**L** it is a multiple of 7
M it has remainder 1 when divided by 4	**N** its units digit is greater than 5	**O** the sum of its digits is 10

Write down a list of **all** the letters of statements that fit your number.

⊙ Swap your lists. The winner is the player who first works out the other player's number.

● Points to remember

⊙ A **sequence** of numbers follows a rule.

⊙ If a sequence has equal steps, you can find the rule and the next terms.

⊙ You can make a sequence if you know the **first term** and the **rule**.

⊙ Use what you know about numbers to make statements about numbers.

2 Function machines

This lesson will help you to find inputs and outputs of function machines.

Exercise 2

A **function machine** has a **rule** that changes the **input** to the **output**.

The starting number is the **input**. The **output** is the finishing number.

This is a one-step function machine.

input → | add 11 | → output

If you put in 6 (the input) then add 11, you get the number 17 (the output).

This is a two-step function machine.

input → | multiply by 2 | → | add 5 | → output

If you put in 2 (the input), multiply it by 2 then add 5, you get the number 9 (the output).

---

1 Put the input 8 through each one-step function machine.

  a input → | add 7 | → output   **b** input → | subtract 6 | → output

  c input → | divide by 2 | → output   **d** input → | multiply by 3 | → output

  e input → | add 20 | → output   **f** input → | subtract 8 | → output

2 Put the input 5 through each two-step function machine.

  a input → | × 3 | → | + 2 | → output   **b** input → | × 5 | → | − 1 | → output

  c input → | + 3 | → | × 2 | → output   **d** input → | − 3 | → | × 10 | → output

  e input → | ÷ 5 | → | + 6 | → output   **f** input → | ÷ 2 | → | + 1 | → output

3 Patrick's rule is 'double then add 1'.

Write five numbers of your own as the input numbers.
Work out the output for each input.

4 **a** Write down your own two-step rule.
Write three numbers as input numbers.
Work out the output for each input.

b What happens to each of these input numbers when you use your rule?

   i 5   **ii** 10   **iii** 0   **iv** 100

5 The output is 36. Work out the input.

a input $(x) \longrightarrow$ | add 8 | $\longrightarrow$ output (y)

b input $(x) \longrightarrow$ | subtract 5 | $\longrightarrow$ output (y)

c input $(x) \longrightarrow$ | multiply by 6 | $\longrightarrow$ output (y)

d input $(x) \longrightarrow$ | divide by 2 | $\longrightarrow$ output (y)

e input $(x) \longrightarrow$ | multiply by 5 | $\longrightarrow$ | add 6 | $\longrightarrow$ output (y)

f input $(x) \longrightarrow$ | multiply by 4 | $\longrightarrow$ | subtract 4 | $\longrightarrow$ output (y)

g input $(x) \longrightarrow$ | add 2 | $\longrightarrow$ | multiply by 6 | $\longrightarrow$ output (y)

Extension problem

6 A taxi ride costs £5 plus 75p per kilometre.

This spreadsheet works out the cost in **pence** of a taxi ride.

Use the spreadsheet to work out the cost in **pounds** (£) of these rides:

  a 3 km   **b** 6 km

  c 10 km   **d** 100 km

A	B	C
Input	Multiply by 75 and add 500	Output
1	$\longrightarrow$	575
2	$\longrightarrow$	650
3	$\longrightarrow$	725
4	$\longrightarrow$	800
5	$\longrightarrow$	875

⊙ Points to remember

- ⊙ A **function machine** has a rule that changes the **input** to the **output**.
- ⊙ Work through a function machine from the input to the output by following the arrows.
- ⊙ You can use the labels x for the input and y for the output.

3 Finding the rule

This lesson will help you to work out the function machine from the numbers input and output.

Exercise 3

In this exercise you will work like a detective looking for clues to help you work out functions.

If you have only one input and output number, there may be several possible rules.

Example 1

$3 \rightarrow \boxed{?} \rightarrow 12$

This rule could be 'multiply by 4' or it could be 'add 9'.

Example 2

$2 \rightarrow \boxed{?} \rightarrow 10$

$4 \rightarrow \boxed{?} \rightarrow 20$

This rule can only be 'multiply by 5'.

Example 3

$2 \rightarrow \boxed{?} \rightarrow \boxed{?} \rightarrow 7$

There are lots of possible answers.

Two possibilities are:
'multiply by 3 and add 1'
'add 9 and subtract 4'.

1. What are the rules for these one-step machines? Write one possibility for each machine.

   a $5 \rightarrow \boxed{?} \rightarrow 15$ b $8 \rightarrow \boxed{?} \rightarrow 2$ c $6 \rightarrow \boxed{?} \rightarrow 13$

   d $9 \rightarrow \boxed{?} \rightarrow 4$ e $7 \rightarrow \boxed{?} \rightarrow 21$ f $17 \rightarrow \boxed{?} \rightarrow 8$

2. What are the rules for these two-step machines? Write two possibilities for each machine.

   a $2 \rightarrow \boxed{?} \rightarrow \boxed{?} \rightarrow 12$ b $8 \rightarrow \boxed{?} \rightarrow \boxed{?} \rightarrow 9$ c $5 \rightarrow \boxed{?} \rightarrow \boxed{?} \rightarrow 16$

   d $7 \rightarrow \boxed{?} \rightarrow \boxed{?} \rightarrow 4$ e $3 \rightarrow \boxed{?} \rightarrow \boxed{?} \rightarrow 7$ f $10 \rightarrow \boxed{?} \rightarrow \boxed{?} \rightarrow 24$

3 What is the rule that works for **all** these one-step function machines?

$3 \rightarrow \boxed{?} \rightarrow 18$ $5 \rightarrow \boxed{?} \rightarrow 30$

$4 \rightarrow \boxed{?} \rightarrow 24$ $10 \rightarrow \boxed{?} \rightarrow 60$

$7 \rightarrow \boxed{?} \rightarrow 42$ $12 \rightarrow \boxed{?} \rightarrow 72$

4 Look at this set of inputs and outputs.

Write down the rule. It has two steps.

Now work out the output for each of these input numbers.

input		output
5	→	16
1	→	4
2	→	7

a 10   b 7   c 3

d 0   e 11   f 100

Extension problems

5 What is the rule that works for **all** these two-step function machines?

$2 \rightarrow \boxed{?} \rightarrow \boxed{?} \rightarrow 9$ $5 \rightarrow \boxed{?} \rightarrow \boxed{?} \rightarrow 21$

$7 \rightarrow \boxed{?} \rightarrow \boxed{?} \rightarrow 29$ $9 \rightarrow \boxed{?} \rightarrow \boxed{?} \rightarrow 37$

$3 \rightarrow \boxed{?} \rightarrow \boxed{?} \rightarrow 13$ $10 \rightarrow \boxed{?} \rightarrow \boxed{?} \rightarrow 41$

6 Find the rule for each set of inputs and outputs.

a

input		output
1	→	5
10	→	32
3	→	11
12	→	38

b

input		output
5	→	16
1	→	4
2	→	7
	→	

c

input		output
5	→	16
1	→	4
2	→	7
	→	

Points to remember

⊙ If you have only one input and output for a function machine, you can usually find more than one possible rule.

⊙ When you have several inputs and outputs for a function machine, you can find a unique rule.

4 Mapping diagrams

This lesson will help you to record inputs and outputs in tables and mapping diagrams.

 Did you know that...?

Leonhard Euler was a Swiss mathematician.

He invented the idea of mappings.

Leonhard was taught maths at home by his father and his father's friends. He was lucky to know lots of people who were expert at maths.

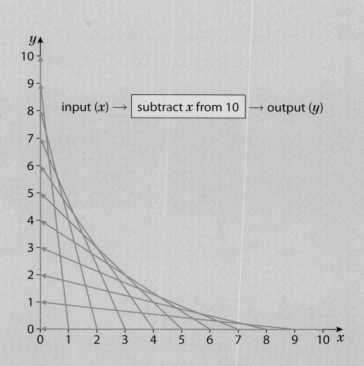

input (x) $\longrightarrow$ [subtract x from 10] $\longrightarrow$ output (y)

Leonhard Euler (1707–1783)

Exercise 4

Inputs and outputs of a function machine can be recorded in a **table**.

input (x) $\longrightarrow$ [add 7] $\longrightarrow$ output (y)

input (x)	1	4	7	9
output (y)	8	11	14	16

The inputs and outputs of a function machine can also be recorded as a **mapping diagram**.

input (x) $\longrightarrow$ [add 7] $\longrightarrow$ output (y)

input x	$\longrightarrow$ [add 7] $\longrightarrow$	output y
1	$\longrightarrow$	8
4	$\longrightarrow$	11
7	$\longrightarrow$	14
9	$\longrightarrow$	16

1 You need **A2.2 Resource sheet 4.1**.
Complete the tables for one-step function machines.

2 You need **A2.2 Resource sheet 4.1**.
Complete the tables for two-step function machines.

3 You need **A2.2 Resource sheet 4.2**.
Complete the mapping diagrams.

4 Find the one-step rule for each mapping diagram.

a

input x →	?	→ output y
1	→	7
2	→	8
3	→	9
4	→	10
5	→	11

b

input x →	?	→ output y
1	→	8
2	→	16
3	→	24
4	→	32
5	→	40

Extension problem

5 Find the two-step rule for this
mapping diagram.

input x →	?	→	?	→output y
1		→		3
2		→		5
3		→		7
4		→		9
5		→		11

⊙ **Points to remember**

⊙ You can record the inputs (x) and outputs (y) of a function machine in a
table or a **mapping diagram**.

5 Coordinates

This lesson will help you to plot and read points on a grid.

 Did you know that...?

The Frenchman **René Descartes** (1596–1650) used a grid to plot points.

The points are called 'Cartesian coordinates', but we usually just say 'coordinates'.

A region of the Moon is named after Descartes. This is where Apollo 16 landed in 1972.

Exercise 5

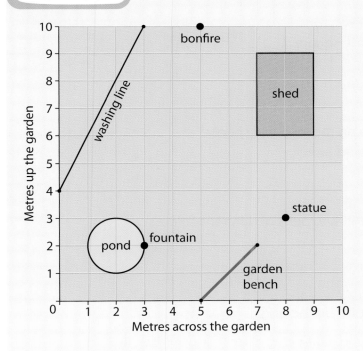

Here is a plan of Asif's back garden.

To get to statue, you go 8 metres across the garden and 3 metres up.

(8, 3) are the **coordinates** of the statue.

To get to bonfire, you go 5 metres across the garden and 10 metres up.

(5, 10) are the coordinates of the bonfire.

The order of the numbers matters. (5, 10) is **not** the same as (10, 5).

Example 1

What are the coordinates of the fountain?

(3, 2)

Example 2

a   In the garden, what starts at (0, 4) and goes to (3, 10)?

The washing line.

b   What are the coordinates of the four corners of the shed?

(7, 9), (9, 9), (9, 6) and (7, 6)

1. Write the coordinates of the following.

   a the dead tree

   b the swamp

   c the gravestone

   d Hangman Hill

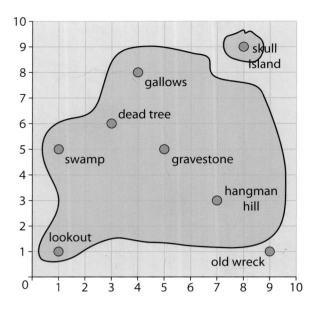

2. What can you find at these coordinates?

   a (8, 9)

   b (9, 1)

   c (1, 1)

   d (4, 8)

3. The buried treasure is half way between the swamp and the gravestone.
   Write its coordinates.

4. The gallows, the dead tree and the gravestone are three of the four corners of a square.
   Harry's hut is at the fourth corner of the square.
   Write its coordinates.

5. You need **A2.2 Resource sheet 5.1**.
   Plot the points using the coordinates on the resource sheet.
   Join the points in order using a ruler and pencil.

6. Work with a partner.
   You need **A2.2 Resource sheet 5.2** and two pens of different colours.

   Play the game **Four in a row**.

   ## Rules

   - One player begins by plotting a point on the grid.

   - The other player then plots a point in a different place using a different colour.

   - Take turns to plot points.

   - Try to get four points in a row.
     But don't forget to stop your opponent from getting four points in a row.

   - The row of four points can be horizontal, vertical or diagonal.

7 **a** AB is the left-hand side of square ABCD.
What are the coordinates of C and D?

b Write the coordinates for the vertices of
another square.

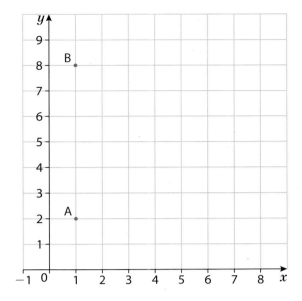

8 **a** AC is the diagonal of square ABCD.
What are the coordinates of points B and D?

b What are the coordinates of the midpoints
of each of the sides of the square ABCD?

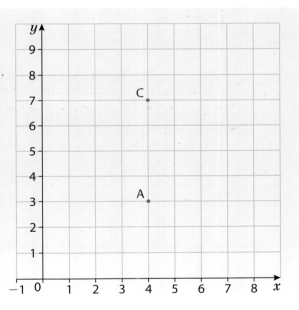

⊙ **Points to remember**

- ⊙ (3, 4) is a pair of **coordinates**.
- ⊙ To plot (3, 4) on a grid, start at (0, 0) and go 3 steps to the right and
  4 steps up.
- ⊙ The order of the numbers matters; the point (3, 4) is not the same
  as the point (4, 3).

6 Graphs

This lesson will help you to plot inputs and outputs as coordinates.

Exercise 6

You can write the inputs and outputs of a function machine as the pair (x, y).

You can plot the points (x, y) on a grid.

You can join the points to get a line graph.

Example

Plot the graph of this function:

input (x) $\longrightarrow$ | add 3 | $\longrightarrow$ output (y)

input (x)	0	1	2	3
output (y)	3	4	5	6
(x, y)	(0, 3)	(1, 4)	(2, 5)	(3, 6)

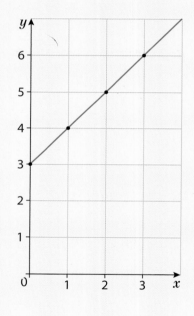

1   Copy and complete the table.

input (x) $\longrightarrow$ | multiply by 3 | $\longrightarrow$ | subtract 1 | $\longrightarrow$ output (y)

input (x)	1	4	7	8	11
output (y)					
(x, y)					

2 Copy and complete the mapping diagram.

input x → [subtract 4] → **output y**   **ordered pairs (x, y)**

6	→	
8	→	
9	→	
11	→	
15	→	

3 You need **A2.2 Resource sheet 6.1**.

Plot each set of coordinates as points on a grid on the resource sheet.

a input (x) → [add 3] → output (y)

(0, 3), (1, 4), (2, 5), (3, 6), (4, 7), (5, 8)

b input (x) → [subtract 1] → output (y)

(1, 0), (2, 1), (3, 2), (4, 3), (5, 4), (6, 5)

c input (x) → [multiply by 2] → output (y)

(0, 0), (1, 2), (2, 4), (3, 6), (4, 8), (5, 10)

d input (x) → [multiply by 3] → [subtract 1] → output (y)

(1, 2), (2, 5), (3, 8), (4, 11), (5, 14)

4 You need another copy of **A2.2 Resource sheet 6.1**.

Plot each set of coordinates as points on a grid on the resource sheet.
Join each set of points to make a straight-line graph.

a input (x) → [add 7] → output (y)

(0, 7), (1, 8), (2, 9), (3, 10), (4, 11), (5, 12)

b input (x) → [subtract 3] → output (y)

(3, 0), (4, 1), (5, 2), (6, 3), (7, 4), (8, 5)

c input (x) → [multiply by 3] → output (y)

(0, 0), (1, 3), (2, 6), (3, 9), (4, 12)

d input (x) → [multiply by 2] → [add 5] → output (y)

(0, 5), (1, 7), (2, 9), (3, 11), (4, 13)

5 The posts of a fence are evenly spaced.

A, B, C and D are the first, second, third and fourth posts of the fence.

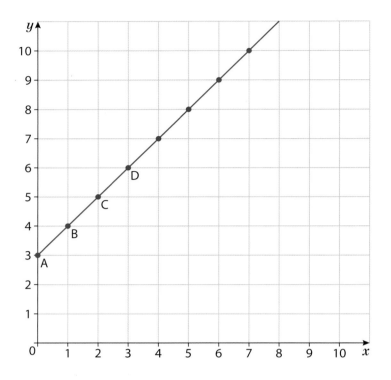

Copy and complete this table for the posts of the fence.
The first post is done for you.

Post number	1	2	3	4	8	10	100
x-coordinate	0						
y-coordinate	3						

Points to remember

- The input x and the output y of a function machine can be written as (x, y).
- You can plot the (x, y) pairs as coordinate points on a grid.
- The points can be joined to make a graph.

How well are you doing?

Can you:

- continue and find missing terms in number sequences?
- find inputs and outputs of functions?
- record inputs and outputs of functions in tables and mapping diagrams?
- read and plot coordinates?

1 *2006 KS2 level 4*

The numbers in this sequence increase by the same amount each time.

1, ☐, ☐, 13

Write the missing numbers.

2 *2002 level 4*

a I can think of three different rules to change **6** to **18**.

$$6 \rightarrow 18$$

Copy and complete these sentences to show what these rules could be.

first rule: **add** …………

second rule: **multiply by** …………

third rule: **multiply by 2 then** …………

b Now I think of a new rule.

The new rule changes 10 to 5 **and** it changes 8 to 4.

$$10 \rightarrow 5 \qquad 8 \rightarrow 4$$

Write what the new rule could be.

3 Copy and complete the table.

input $(x) \rightarrow$ | add 9 | $\rightarrow$ output (y)

input (x)	1	3	5	10	12
output (y)					

4 *2007 Progress Test level 4*

a A rule changes $1\frac{1}{2}$ to $4\frac{1}{2}$.

$1\frac{1}{2}$ ⟶ **?** ⟶ $4\frac{1}{2}$

What could the rule be? Choose two of the answers below.

$+3$ -3 $\times 3$ $\div 3$

b A rule changes 10 to 5.

10 ⟶ **?** ⟶ 5

What could the rule be? Give two different answers.

5 Copy and complete this mapping diagram.

input x →	add 3	→	multiply by 5	→	output y
2		→			
5		→			
6		→			
8		→			

6 *2006 KS2 level 4*

A, B, C and D are the vertices of a rectangle.

A and B are shown on the grid.

D is the point (3, 4).

What are the coordinates of point C?

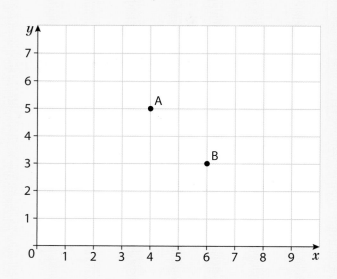

Symmetry and reflection

This unit will help you to:

- reflect a shape in a mirror line;
- draw lines of symmetry on 2D shapes;
- draw the position of a shape after a translation;
- explore symmetry and simple transformations using ICT.

1 Reflection

This lesson will help you to reflect a shape in a mirror line.

Exercise 1

Example

The starting shape is the **object**.
The reflection is the **image**.

Point A is reflected to point X.

A and X are the same distance from the mirror line.
B and Y are the same distance from the mirror line.

The line joining A and X is at right angles to the mirror line.
The line joining B and Y is at right angles to the mirror line.

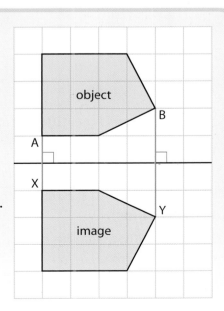

Work with a partner. You will need **G2.3 Resource sheets 1.1 and 1.2**, a ruler and sharp pencil, and a computer with the program **Reflection**.

1. On **G2.3 Resource sheet 1.1**, draw each reflection in the mirror line. Check your answers using the computer program **Line symmetry**.

2. On **G2.3 Resource sheet 1.2**, draw each reflection in the mirror line. Check your answers using the computer program **Line symmetry**.

Extension problems

3. Copy this diagram on squared paper.

    Reflect the shaded shape in line A. Then reflect the shape and its image in line B.

4. Copy this diagram on squared paper.

    Reflect the shaded shape in line C. Then reflect the shape and its image in line D.

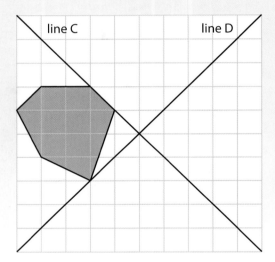

Points to remember

⊙ The starting shape is the **object** and the reflected shape is the **image**.

⊙ In a reflection:
  – the object and image are the same shape and size;
  – matching points on the object and image are the same distance from the **mirror line**;
  – the line joining matching points on the object and image is at right angles to the mirror line.

2 Symmetry

This lesson will help you to recognise and draw lines of symmetry.

Exercise 2

These pictures show that reflection happens in nature.
Each picture has a line of symmetry where the real object is reflected in the water.

Example

Draw all the lines of symmetry in a rectangle and a regular pentagon.

This rectangle has 2 lines of symmetry.   This regular pentagon has 5 lines of symmetry.

1 Look at this picture of a butterfly
   sitting on a garden plant.

   a Is the whole picture symmetrical?

   b Are the patterns on the butterfly
      symmetrical?

2 These road signs are from the Highway Code.
For each road sign write how many lines of symmetry there are.

a No entry

b Traffic lights

c Risk of ice

d Keep left

3 Imran took some pictures of car badges in the town car park.
For each badge, write how many lines of symmetry it has.

a Mercedes

b Ford

c Citroen

d Mitsubishi

e Rover

f Honda

g Peugeot

h Audi

i Volkswagen

j Fiat

k BMW

l Toyota

4 Write the number of lines of symmetry in each of these shapes.

a regular octagon

b seven-pointed star

c regular pentagon

5 Copy each shape on squared paper.
Colour one more square so that the completed shape has only one line of symmetry.
For each shape there are two possible solutions. Draw them both.

a   b   c

6 Copy this shape on squared paper.
Shade two more squares so that the completed
shape has two lines of symmetry.

Extension problem

7 This L-shape is made from 3 squares.

You can put two L-shapes together like this
to make a shape with one line of symmetry.

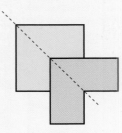

a Draw a different shape made from two L-shapes. It must have only one
line of symmetry.

b Draw a different shape made from two L-shapes. It must have two lines of symmetry.

⊙ **Points to remember**

⊙ A **line of symmetry** or **mirror line** divides a shape into half so that one
half folds exactly on top of the other half.

⊙ A regular polygon has the same number of lines of symmetry as sides.

3 Translation

This lesson will help you to translate a shape from one position to another.

Did you know that...?

This pattern of floor tiles is from Australia.

The basic shape is a lizard. The lizards have been repeated and fitted together so that there are no gaps between them.

The pattern is known as a **tessellation**.

A famous Dutch artist who used tessellations to make patterns was **M. C. Escher** (1898–1972).

Exercise 3

This pattern of Arabic tiles has been made by sliding a shape in a straight line to a new position. This kind of movement is called a **translation**.

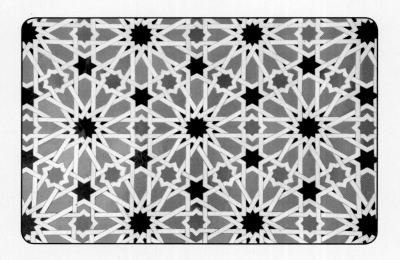

Example

Translate the shape 6 right, 2 down.

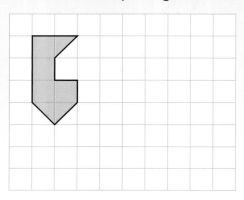

All points of the object move 6 right and 2 down.

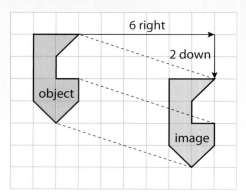

1   Copy this shape in the middle of some squared paper.
    Translate the object:

    a   2 right, 5 up. Label the image A.

    b   2 left, 6 up. Label the image B.

    c   0 right, 3 up. Label the image C.

    d   4 left, 1 down. Label the image D.

    e   0 left, 5 down. Label the image E.

    f   3 right, 2 down. Label the image F.

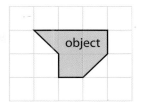

2   In this diagram the object has been translated
    to A, B, C, and so on.

    For each image A to J, write the translation.

    Remember to write left or right movements first.

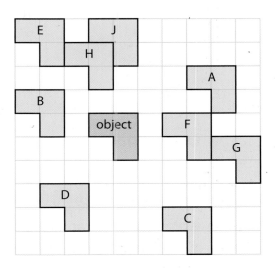

3   In this diagram the object has been translated many times to create a tessellation.

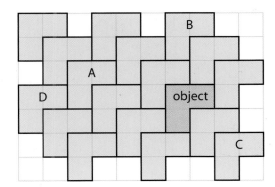

    Describe the translation from the object to:

    a   image A   b   image B

    c   image C   d   image D

4 Copy the diagram on squared paper.

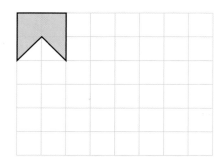

Complete the diagram to show how the shape will tessellate.
Draw at least eight more shapes.

Extension problem

5 Each of these shapes can be translated so that there is no gap between each image.
For each shape:

○ Copy the shape onto squared paper. Label it 'object'.

○ Draw more of the shapes to show how they will tessellate.

○ Label six of the tessellated shapes A to F.

○ Write down the translation needed to move the object to shape A.

○ Repeat with shape B, then C, then D, then E, then F.

a 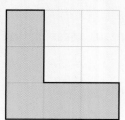   b 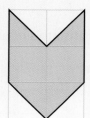   c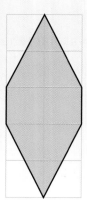

◉ Points to remember

◉ When an object is **translated**, every point of the object moves the same
distance in the same direction.

◉ The size and shape of the object and image are identical.

How well are you doing?

You will need some isometric paper and squared paper.

1 *2004 level 3*

When you fold a square along a diagonal, you see a triangle.

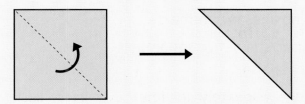

a What do you see when you fold a rectangle along a diagonal?

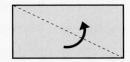

Write the letter of the correct answer below.

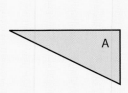
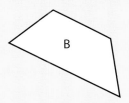
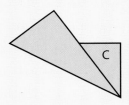
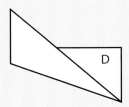

b Three different shapes below are folded along a line of symmetry.
For each shape, the dashed line is the fold line.

Copy each shape onto isometric paper.
Draw what the shape looked like before it was folded.

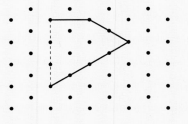
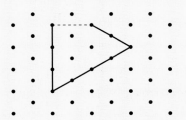
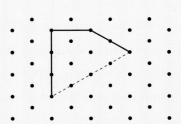

2 *2005 level 4*

Copy each shape on squared paper.

Shade one more square on each grid so that each shape has one line of symmetry.

a
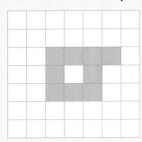
b
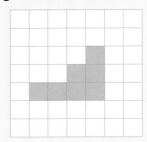

3 *2004 Progress Test level 4*

Look at the square grid.

Five squares are shaded to make a shape.

The shape has no lines of symmetry.

On squared paper, shade five squares to make a different shape.

The shape must have exactly one line of symmetry.

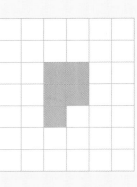

4 Write down the translation that moves shape A to shape B.

What is the translation that moves shape B to shape A?

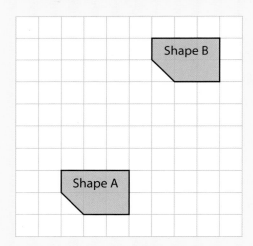

Decimals and measures

This unit will help you to:

- ⊙ work with measurements to one or two decimal places;
- ⊙ know simple fractions of 1 kilometre, 1 metre, 1 kilogram or 1 litre;
- ⊙ multiply and divide decimals by 10, 100 or 1000;
- ⊙ convert between units of measurement;
- ⊙ read scales;
- ⊙ use 12-hour clocks and work out time intervals;
- ⊙ write a division with a remainder as a fraction or decimal;
- ⊙ solve word problems, including problems involving remainders.

1 Metres, centimetres and millimetres

This lesson will help you to work with metres and centimetres using decimals with one or two places.

Exercise 1

 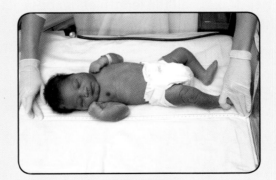 

Kilometres, metres, centimetres and millimetres are used to measure lengths, heights and distances.

- ⊙ There are 10 millimetres in 1 centimetre, so 17 millimetres is 1.7 centimetres.
- ⊙ There are 100 centimetres in 1 metre, so 294 centimetres is 2.94 metres

1 What must you add to each of these lengths to make 1 metre?

  a 40 cm   b 72 cm   c 9 cm   d 23.5 cm

2 Change to centimetres.

   a 7 m   b 9.1 m   c 0.73 m   d 20 m

3 Change to metres.

   a 175 cm   b 26 cm   c 108 cm   d 9 cm

4 Change to millimetres.

   a 27 cm   b 8.5 cm   c 10 cm   d 0.7 cm

5 Change to centimetres.

   a 95 mm   b 460 mm   c 30 mm   d 8 mm

6 Work these out. Give your answers in metres.

   a What length is 19 cm less than 2 metres?

   b What length is 3 metres 58 centimetres less than 5 metres?

   c What length is 4 metres 68 centimetres less than 9 metres 19 centimetres?

7 Camilla's desk is 1 metre 52 centimetres long.

   a Her bookshelf is twice as long as her desk.
      How long is her bookshelf? Give your answer in metres.

   b The width of her desk is half the length of her desk.
      How wide is her desk? Give your answer in metres.

   c Her bed is 2.09 metres long.
      How much longer than her desk is her bed?
      Write your answer in centimetres.

8 The diagram is not drawn accurately.

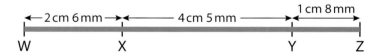

   a Work out the length in centimetres of:
      i WY   ii XZ

   b What is the length of WZ in millimetres?

   c How much longer in millimetres is XY than YZ?

   d How much longer in centimetres is XY than WX?

9 What is the height of this block?
Give your answer in metres.

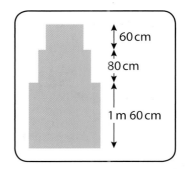

60 cm
80 cm
1 m 60 cm

10 ABCD is a rectangle.
CD is 8 cm. DA is 4 cm.

a Measure AC. Write its length in
centimetres, then in millimetres.

b Measure DF. Write its length in
centimetres, then in millimetres.

c Measure ED. Write its length in
centimetres, then in millimetres.

d Measure EF. Write its length in
centimetres, then in millimetres.

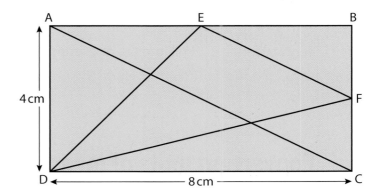

4 cm

8 cm

Extension problems

Did you know that...?

Harriet Quimby was the first woman to fly alone across the English Channel.
She did this in 1912, two days after the Titanic sank.

She died 3 months later when she fell from an aeroplane into the sea.

Harriet designed her own flight suit in purple satin.
She wore it whenever she flew.

11 This photo of a stamp shows Harriet Quimby.
It measures 42 mm by 29 mm.

What is its perimeter in centimetres?

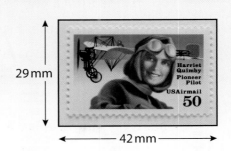

29 mm

42 mm

12 Copy and complete these sentences.

    a 150 mm is the same as … cm.

    b 150 cm is the same as … m.

    c 150 m is the same as … km.

Points to remember

⊙ 4.07 m is 4 metres and 7 centimetres or 407 cm.

⊙ 3.2 m is 3 metres 20 centimetres or 320 cm.

⊙ 2.9 cm is 2 centimetres and 9 millimetres or 29 mm.

⊙ When an answer is a measurement, include the units.

2 Converting units of measurement

This lesson will help you to multiply and divide by 10, 100 or 1000, and convert units of measuremen.

Exercise 2

To change one metric unit to another you need to know these relationships.

Length
10 mm = 1 cm
100 cm = 1 m
1000 mm = 1 m
1000 m = 1 km

Weight
1000 g = 1 kg

Capacity/volume
1000 ml = 1 litre

You only need to multiply or divide by 10, 100 or 1000.

☺ When you change from a unit to a larger unit you divide.

☺ When you change from a unit to a smaller unit you multiply.

To convert lengths, you can use this diagram:

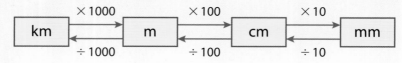

Example

Change 2540 g to kg.

2540 g = 2540 ÷ 1000 kg   Kilograms are larger than grams.

     = 2.54 kg   As 1000 g = 1 kg, divide by 1000.

1. Play the game of **Target 5** with a partner.
   You need two dice.

   Rules

   ◉ Roll the two dice.

   ◉ Make two two-digit numbers, e.g. with 5 and 6 make 65 and 56.

   ◉ Now each player makes two decimals by dividing either of the two-digit numbers by
   10 or 100, e.g. with 65 and 56 you can make any two of these:

   $65 \div 10 = 6.5$ $65 \div 100 = 0.65$ $56 \div 10 = 5.6$ $56 \div 100 = 0.56$

   ◉ Add your two decimals. So if you have made 5.6 and 0.65, work out $5.6 + 0.65 = 6.25$.

   ◉ The player with the total nearest to 5 scores 1 point.

   ◉ The winner is the player with the most points when time is up.

2. Work out the answers **without using your calculator**.

   a 46×100 b 8.3×10 c 0.25×1000

   d 320×10 e 5.9×100 f 0.03×1000

3. Work out the answers **without using your calculator**.

   a $720 \div 10$ b $91 \div 10$ c $54 \div 100$

   d $2300 \div 100$ e $480 \div 1000$ f $26 \div 1000$

4. Change to kilometres.

   a 6000 m   b 3500 m   c 800 m

   Change to metres.

   d 9 km   e 2.5 km   f 0.7 km

5. Change to kilograms.

   a 2000 g   b 1800 g   c 500 g

   Change to grams.

   d 6 kg   e 4.8 kg   f 12 kg

6 Change to litres.

   a 9000 ml   b 1500 ml   c 750 ml

   Change to millilitres.

   d 2 litres   e 1.25 litres   f 0.6 litres

7 A cup holds 250 ml of soup.
   How many cups of soup can you get from 1 litre?

8 A bottle of squash contains 1.2 litres.
   John uses 350 ml to make drinks.
   How many litres of squash are left in the bottle?

9 A jug holds $1\frac{1}{2}$ litres of juice.
   Amy pours 300 ml juice into each of four glasses.
   How many millilitres of juice are left in the jug?

10 Peter bought 1 kg of carrots.
   He cooked 425 g of them.
   How many grams of carrots did Peter have left?

11 Liz has 200 g of flour in a jar.
   She puts another $1\frac{1}{2}$ kg of flour into the jar.
   How many kilograms of flour are in the jar now?

Extension problem

12 Sam wants to send three of these four parcels to his aunt.

   The parcels weigh 6.5 kg, 7.2 kg, 6.4 kg, 6.1 kg.

   a Which three parcels have a total weight nearest to but less than 20 kg?

   b How many grams less than 20 kg are the three parcels?

⊙ Points to remember

- ⊙ Multiplying by 10 moves the digits one place to the left.
  Dividing by 10 moves the digits one place to the right.
  An empty place is filled with 0.
- ⊙ When you multiply or divide by 100, the digits move two places.
- ⊙ When you multiply or divide by 1000, the digits move three places.

3 Reading scales

This lesson will help you to read scales on measuring equipment.

Exercise 3

When you read a scale, work out what the units are and what each small interval represents.

Example 1

This ruler measures the length of the line. The line is 7 cm long.

Example 2

This **measuring jug** measures the volume of liquid in the jug.

The units on the jug are millilitres (ml).

500 ml is half a litre.

Example 3

This thermometer measures your body temperature.

The units are degrees Celsius.

The thermometer shows a normal temperature of 37 °C

1   What is the weight of each parcel?

a   b   c

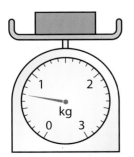   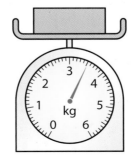   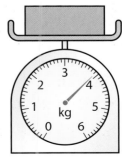

(2) What weight is shown on each scale?

a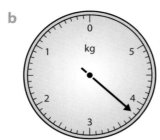

b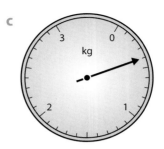

c

(3) Estimate the readings on these scales as accurately as possible.

a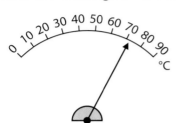

b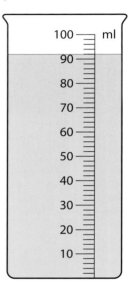

c

(4) What is the length of each pencil?

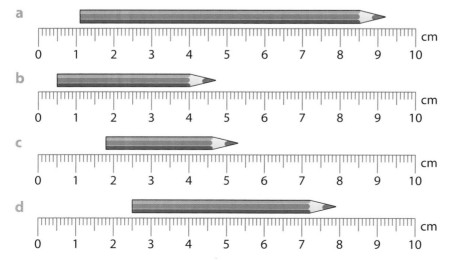

a

b

c

d

5 The arrow on the scale shows the weight of two bags of shopping.

6 kg   7 kg   8 kg ↑   9 kg

   a How much do the two bags of shopping weigh in kilograms?

   b One bag is taken off the scales. This bag weighs 2.5 kg.
      What is the weight of the other bag?

6 The arrow shows the weight of some flour on some scales.

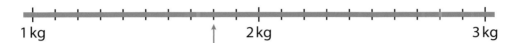

1 kg   ↑   2 kg   3 kg

600 g more flour is added to the scales.
What is the total weight of the flour **in kilograms**?

7 Here is a scale from 0 to 2 kilograms.

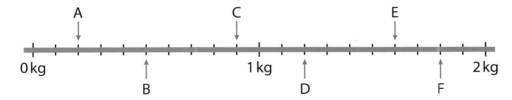

0 kg   1 kg   2 kg

The arrows A to F show the weights of six parcels.
What is the weight of each of the parcels **in grams**?

Extension problem

8 The diagram shows a temperature scale marked in degrees Celsius (°C) and in degrees Fahrenheit (°F).

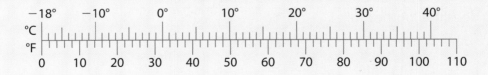

   a Estimate the temperature in °C when the temperature is 80 °F.

   b Estimate the temperature in °F when the temperature is 0 °C.

   c Estimate the temperature in °C when the temperature is 10 °F.

   d Estimate the temperature in °F when the temperature is 40 °C.

Points to remember

⊙ To read a scale, first decide what each interval represents.

⊙ Work out the values of the marks close to the pointer.

⊙ If the pointer lies between two marks, estimate the reading.

4 Time

This lesson will help you to use 12-hour clocks and work out time intervals.

Exercise 4

An **analogue** clock or watch has hands.
It show **12-hour clock** times.

This clock shows twenty minutes past eight.
It doesn't tell us whether this is morning or afternoon.

To do this, we use **am** for times before noon (midday)
and **pm** for times after noon.

A **digital** clock or watch has a number display.

A colon (:) separates the hours from the minutes.

The letters AM show that the time is 11 o'clock in the morning.

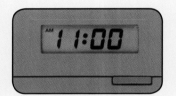

A **time line** helps you to work out time intervals.

Example

A car journey starts at 10:35 am and finishes at 3:50 pm.
How long does the journey take?

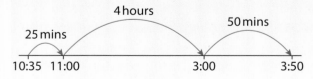

From 10:35 am to 11:00 am is 25 minutes.

From 11:00 am to 3:00 pm is 4 hours.

From 3:00 pm to 3:50 pm is 50 minutes.

The journey time is the total of 4 hours, 50 minutes and 25 minutes,
which is 5 hours and 15 minutes.

1. 8:50 am is 10 minutes to 9 in the morning.
   What are these times?

   a 5:15 am   b 3:27 pm

   c 11:42 am   d 4:56 pm

2. Quarter to 8 in the evening is 7:45 pm in 12-hour clock time.
   Write these times in 12-hour clock time.

   a 4 o'clock in the morning   b Quarter past 7 in the evening

   c 3 minutes past midnight   d 22 minutes past 8 in the morning

   e 6 o'clock in the afternoon   f Quarter to 10 in the morning

   g Half past 12 in the afternoon   h 25 minutes to 8 in the evening

   i 14 minutes to 6 in the morning   j 3 minutes to midnight

3. Change these times to minutes.

   a 3 hours   b 10 hours

   c 4 hours 15 minutes   d 2 hours 50 minutes

4. Change these times to hours.

   a 2 days   b 240 minutes

   c 300 minutes   d 1 week

5. How many minutes are there in a day?

6. George worked in his garden.
   He worked 3 hours 20 minutes in the morning and 2 hours 50 minutes in the afternoon.
   How long in total did he work in his garden?

7. Rashid made a lemon drizzle cake.
   It took 1 hour 50 minutes to bake.
   It finished baking at 1:05 pm.
   At what time did Rashid start baking the cake?

8. A film starts at 6:45 pm.
   It lasts 2 hours and 35 minutes.
   At what time will the film finish?

9   A flight from Glasgow to Ottawa takes
12 hours 40 minutes.
It takes off at 9:35 am.
What time is it in Glasgow when the
plane lands?

10   A school's day starts at 8:35 am.
The school's day ends at 3:20 pm.
How long does the school's day last?

11   A train leaves Newark at 4:46 pm and arrives in London at 5:28 pm.
How long does the journey take?

12   Here is part of a bus timetable.

a   How long does the bus take from Fatherham
to the Station?

b   Sue arrived at Ham Post Office at 9:53.
How long did she wait for the bus?

c   Simon caught the bus from Wick to Green Park.
How long was his bus journey?

Bus stop	Time of bus (am)
Fatherham	9:45
Wick	9:58
Binley Church	10:05
Ham Post Office	10:08
Green Park	10:17
Station	10:25

Extension problem

13   A prize in a competition will use about 1 000 000 seconds of your time.
Which prize is it?

A   One week at Disney World

B   10 days in Spain

C   A fortnight skiing

D   A month on a cruise

E   A year on a trip around the world

Explain your answer.

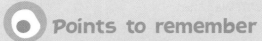
Points to remember

⊙ 00:00 is midnight and 12:00 is midday or noon.

⊙ From midnight to noon is am and is the morning.

⊙ From noon to midnight is pm and is the afternoon.

⊙ When you write the time, use a colon to separate the hours from the minutes, e.g. 10:15 am.

⊙ A time line can help with time calculations.

5 Remainders

This lesson will help you to write a remainder as a fraction or decimal.

Exercise 5

5 pizzas are shared equally between 2 people.
Each person gets 2 whole pizzas.
One pizza is left over.

So the answer to 5 ÷ 2 is 2 r 1.

The pizza that is left over is divided into two.
Each person gets half.

So the answer to 5 ÷ 2 is $2\frac{1}{2}$.

Since $\frac{1}{2} = 0.5$, we can also write the answer to 5 ÷ 2 as 2.5.

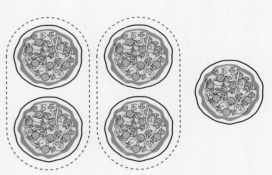

1   When 8 is divided by 3, the remainder is 2.
What is the remainder after each division?

   a   20 ÷ 6   b   25 ÷ 7   c   41 ÷ 8   d   52 ÷ 9

   e   49 ÷ 5   f   39 ÷ 4   g   123 ÷ 10   h   20 ÷ 18

   i   67 ÷ 11

2   Work out each division.
Give each answer as a whole number and fraction.

   a   5 ÷ 2   b   29 ÷ 10   c   10 ÷ 3   d   25 ÷ 4

   e   17 ÷ 5   f   21 ÷ 2   g   31 ÷ 4   h   14 ÷ 3

   i   8 ÷ 5   j   23 ÷ 7   k   50 ÷ 9   l   47 ÷ 8

3 Write each of these as a decimal.

a $\frac{1}{2}$ b $\frac{1}{4}$ c $\frac{1}{5}$ d $\frac{1}{10}$

e $\frac{2}{5}$ f $\frac{1}{100}$ g $\frac{7}{100}$ h $\frac{3}{5}$

i $\frac{9}{10}$ j $\frac{3}{4}$ k $\frac{63}{100}$ l $\frac{4}{5}$

4 Write each of these as a decimal.

a $2\frac{1}{2}$ b $5\frac{1}{4}$ c $9\frac{3}{10}$ d $8\frac{3}{5}$

e $12\frac{3}{4}$ f $5\frac{21}{100}$

5 Work out each division. Give each answer as a decimal.

a $9 \div 2$ b $67 \div 10$ c $30 \div 4$ d $23 \div 5$

e $347 \div 100$ f $31 \div 5$ g $34 \div 8$ h $104 \div 5$

i $50 \div 8$ j $51 \div 10$ k $37 \div 5$ l $30 \div 12$

6 Solve these problems **without using your calculator**.
Write down the calculation you need to do. Work out the answer.

a Four packets of sugar cost £1.44.
   What is the cost of one packet of sugar?

b The cost for three people to go skating is £8.70.
   What is the cost for one person?

c £27.50 is shared equally among five children.
   How much money does each child get?

d Four birthday cakes cost £33.
   What is the cost of one birthday cake?

e Ella bought six pairs of jeans.
   They were all the same price.
   She paid £123.
   What did one pair of jeans cost?

(7) Play the game of **Remainders** with a partner.
You need two dice, one pack of digit cards from 1 to 8
and one pack from 1 to 9.

Rules

- Shuffle the cards. Put them face down in a pile.

- Take turns.

- Roll the dice and find the total.

- Draw two cards and make a two-digit number.
  For example, with 7 and 2 you can choose to make 27 or 72.

- Divide your two-digit number by your dice total.

- The remainder is your score for that turn. Watch out – it might be zero!

- Put your two cards back at the bottom of the pile.

- The winner is the first player to get a total score of 35.

Extension problems

Use your calculator.

(8) A meal in a restaurant costs the same for each person.
For 11 people the total cost is £256.85.
What is the total cost for 12 people?

(9) The cost for using a minibus is £1.38 for each kilometre.
9 friends go on a 132 kilometre journey.
They share the cost equally.
How much does each person pay?

 Points to remember

- When you divide by 10, any remainder is in tenths.
  A remainder of 7 can be represented as $\frac{7}{10}$ or 0.7.

- When you divide by 2, any remainder is $\frac{1}{2}$ or 0.5.

- When you divide by 4, any remainder is $\frac{1}{4}$ or 0.25,
  $\frac{2}{4} = \frac{1}{2}$ or 0.5, or $\frac{3}{4}$ or 0.75.

6 Word problems

This lesson will help you to solve word problems, including problems involving remainders.

Did you know that...?

Lots of jobs involve taking measurements to solve real problems.

People have to decide what units and what measuring equipment they will use.

Exercise 6

To solve word problems, you need to decide which operations to use.
If you use a calculator, you must make sense of the calculator display.

Example

96 Year 7 pupils are going on a visit by minibus.
Each bus has seats for 9 pupils.
How many buses are needed to seat all the pupils?

To work out how many buses are needed, calculate 96 ÷ 9 = 10 r 6.

If the school ordered 10 minibuses, 6 pupils would be left over.
To seat all 96 pupils, the school must order 10 + 1 = 11 minibuses.

1. Write the metric units that you would use to measure:
   a the length of a person's hand
   b the weight of a mouse
   c the distance from Belfast to Dublin
   d a tablespoon of lemon juice
   e the height of a building
   f the area of a postcard.

2   Are these statements sensible? Write **Yes** or **No** for each statement.

a   The headteacher of my school is 3 metres tall.

b   David walks 950 metres to school.

c   The football pitch is 1750 centimetres long.

d   The classroom door is 1000 millimetres high.

e   An orange weighs about 1.2 kg.

f   Mary drank 350 millilitres of coffee at breakfast time.

Do questions 3 and 4 **without using your calculator**.

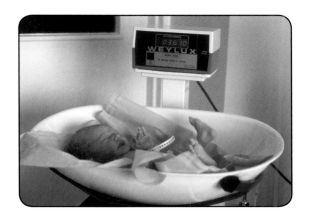

3   a   Kate is a baby. She has 170 ml of milk
          five times each day.
          How much milk does she have each day?

     b   Kate was 48 cm long when she was born.
          She is now 0.5 m tall.
          How many centimetres has she grown?

     c   Kate was 3.4 kg when she was born.
          Since then she has put on 350 g in weight
          each week for 4 weeks.
          What is her weight now?

4   a   The Jones family went to Spain.
          They bought three cheap plane tickets.
          The total cost was £157.20.
          What was the cost of one ticket?

     b   The family took three cases on holiday.
          The cases weighed 24.3 kg, 22.8 kg and 19.25 kg.
          What was the total weight of the cases?

     c   The taxi to the airport cost £27.80.
          Mr and Mrs Jones shared the cost equally.
          How much did each of them pay?

     d   At the airport, Mrs Jones bought 3 bags of crisps.
          She paid a £2 coin and got 89p change.
          What was the cost of one bag of crisps?

You can **use your calculator** for questions 5 and 6.

5   a   A machine fills 287 tins of paint in an hour.
How many tins does it fill in 14 hours?

      b   A paint tin holds 5 litres of paint.
327 litres of paint is to go into tins.
How many tins will be filled?

      c   A tin of paint costs £12.39. A brush costs £4.17.
Find the cost of 16 tins of paint and 3 brushes.

      d   Roger is a decorator.
He gets paid £6.40 for each hour of painting.
How much does he get paid for $35\frac{1}{2}$ hours?

      e   A 1 litre tin of paint will cover 18 square metres.
Tom wants to paint 95 square metres of wall.
How many 1 litre tins of paint should he buy?

6   a   Clare buys four DVDs. They are all the same price.
She pays £57.20. What is the cost of one DVD?

      b   William buys three CDs costing £12.50 each.
He also paid £2.80 in bus fares.
How much does he have left from £45?

      c   Tariq buys 16 identical DVD players to sell in his shop.
Their total weight is 13.6 kg.
What is the weight in grams of one DVD player?

      d   What is the cost of 45 CDs at £7.99 each
and 28 DVDs at £12.49 each?

      e   36 CDs fit in a rack. How many racks will hold 400 CDs?

◉ Points to remember

- ◉ Read word problems carefully.
- ◉ Decide what operation to use and what calculation you will do.
- ◉ Write down the calculation.
- ◉ Estimate the answer.
- ◉ Decide whether or not to use a calculator.
- ◉ Include any units in the answer.
- ◉ Check that your answer makes sense.

How well are you doing?

Can you:

- work with measurements to one or two decimal places?
- remember simple fractions of 1 kilometre, 1 metre, 1 kilogram or 1 litre?
- multiply and divide decimals by 10, 100 or 1000?
- convert between units of measurement?
- read scales?
- use 12-hour clocks and work out time intervals?
- write a remainder as a fraction or decimal?
- solve word problems, including problems involving remainders?

Decimals and measures (no calculator)

1 *2004 level 4*

Steve needs to put 1 litre of water in a bucket.
He has a 500 ml jug.

Explain how he can measure 1 litre of water.

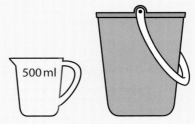

2 *2004 Progress Test level 4*

Peter took part in a long jump competition. He had three jumps. The arrows on the scale show how far he jumped each time.

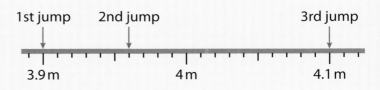

a How far did Peter jump on his 2nd jump?

b Peter jumped further on his 3rd jump than on his 1st jump.
How much further? Write your answer in metres.

3 *2003 Progress Test level 4*

This diagram shows how to change metres into centimetres and millimetres.

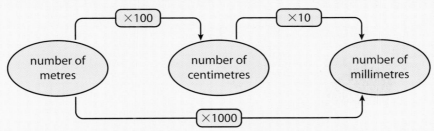

a Change 5 metres into centimetres.   b Change 9 centimetres into millimetres.

c Change 8000 millimetres into metres.

4 *2006 Progress Test level 4*

The scale shows how much five parcels weigh.

All the parcels weigh the same.

How much does one parcel weigh?

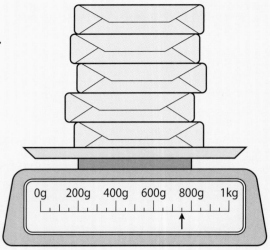

Decimals and measures (calculator allowed)

5 *2006 level 4*

A bottle contains 250 ml of cough mixture.
One adult and one child need to
take cough mixture four times a day
every day for 5 days.
Will there be enough cough mixture
in the bottle?
Explain your answer.

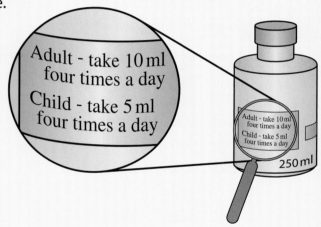

6 *2003 KS2 level 4*

Here are the start and finish times of some friends doing a sponsored walk.

	Start time	Finish time
Claire	9:30	10:55
Ruth	9:35	11:05
Dan	9:40	11:08
Tim	9:45	11:05

How much longer did Claire take than Tim?

Functional skills 2

Arranging your bedroom

This group activity will help you to:

- work out how to tackle an unfamiliar problem;
- choose and use the mathematics needed to solve it;
- explain and justify your solution.

Background

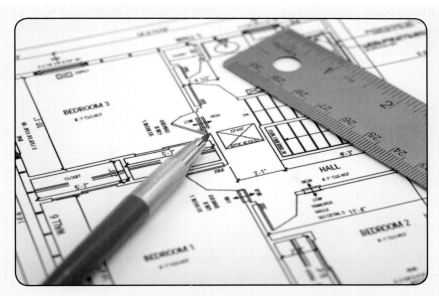

When a family moves into a new house or flat, they have to arrange their furniture in the new rooms.

It is hard work to move furniture in and out of rooms while you decide where you want it to go.

The new rooms may not be the same shape as the old rooms.

Your furniture may not fit in.

You need to think it through beforehand and have a plan ready.

Planning your bedroom

Imagine moving to a new home.

Here is a plan of your new bedroom.

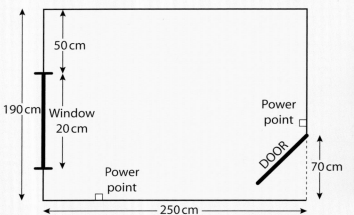

Use a scale of 1 millimetre to 1 centimetre to draw a plan of your bedroom.

Mark the door and the window.

This is a list of the furniture from your old bedroom.

- Bed 185 cm by 90 cm
- Desk 75 cm by 35 cm
- Wardrobe 90 cm by 50 cm
- Chair 46 cm by 46 cm
- Small cupboard 48 cm by 51 cm
- Small cupboard 35 cm by 30 cm
- Round stool with diameter 30 cm

Using the same scale of 1 mm to 1 cm, draw plans of each piece of furniture.

Cut them out and use them to decide which furniture you want and where it will go.

Join up with another group to evaluate your plans. Ask questions like these.

- Is there room for the bedroom door to open?
- If you have chosen a wardrobe or a cupboard, will the doors open?
- Could you open the drawers of the desk?
- If you wanted to sit at the desk, could you do so?
- Would the furniture by the window block out its light?
- Putting a bed under the window might mean it is cold in winter. Would you mind?

Enquiry 1

This unit will help you to:

- ☉ solve a problem by collecting and sorting information;
- ☉ present and interpret information in charts, graphs and diagrams;
- ☉ use the mode and range for a small set of data.

1 Collecting and organising data

This lesson will help you to collect and organise data about a problem.

Did you know that...?

William the Conqueror did the first survey of England in 1086.

He wanted to find out who owned the land. Then he could charge them taxes to pay for his army.

The **Domesday Book** records land owners, their land and whether it was woodland or meadow, the other people who lived on the land, and the numbers of animals, fish, ploughs and buildings.

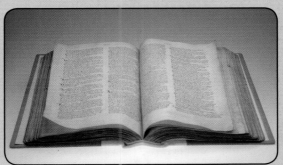

Exercise 1

15 children wrote down their favourite foods.

The results were put into a table.

The **frequency** is the number of times each answer appears in the list.

Favourite food	Frequency
Chips	2
Spaghetti bolognaise	3
Curry	4
Roast dinner	2
Chilli	2
Meatballs	2

1. 20 teenagers wrote down their favourite ice-cream flavour:

   chocolate, strawberry, chocolate, mint, toffee,
   chocolate, chocolate, mint, chocolate, clotted cream,
   clotted cream, mint, toffee, chocolate, mint,
   strawberry, chocolate, chocolate, mint, toffee

   Draw a table to show the results.

2. The 20 teenagers named their favourite snack:

   fruit, toast, popcorn, crackers, vegetables,
   fruit, popcorn, fruit, toast, toast,
   popcorn, toast, fruit, fruit, vegetables,
   toast, pretzels, crackers, toast, toast

   Draw a table to show the results.

3. The 20 teenagers named their favourite drink:

   fizzy drink, fruit juice, tea, fizzy drink, coffee,
   fruit juice, fizzy drink, fizzy drink, fruit juice, water,
   fruit juice, fizzy drink, fruit juice, fruit juice, water,
   fruit juice, tea, fruit juice, tea, fizzy drink

   Draw a table to show the results.

Extension problem

4. Imagine you are planning a party for these 20 teenagers.
   You can choose two ice-cream flavours, two types of snack and
   two drinks to serve at the party.
   What would you serve? Why?

Points to remember

- You can collect data to help find answers to questions.
- Organising information in a **table** makes it easier to understand.
- The **frequency** is the number of times an item occurs.

2 Venn and Carroll diagrams

This lesson will help you to draw and interpret Venn and Carroll diagrams.

Exercise 2

A **Carroll diagram** can be used to sort data using two properties.

The Carroll diagram on the right below shows the same information as the table on the left.

Name	Sport played	TV watched per day
Tom	Football	2 hours
Alana	Netball	1 hour
Rina	Football	$\frac{1}{2}$ hour
Ruth	Swimming	1 hour
Aaron	Tennis	$1\frac{1}{2}$ hours
Zeva	Football	1 hour
Joel	Football	$1\frac{1}{2}$ hours

	Plays football	Does not play football
Watches 1 hour or less of TV a day	Zena Rina	Alana Ruth
Watches more than 1 hour of TV a day	Tom Joel	Aaron

In a **Venn diagram** circles are used to show sets of data.

The Venn diagram on the right below shows the same information as the table on the left.

Name	Number of brothers	Number of sisters
William	1	3
Serena	2	1
Felicity	0	0
Marcos	2	1
Ashley	3	0
Shane	1	2
Petra	0	1

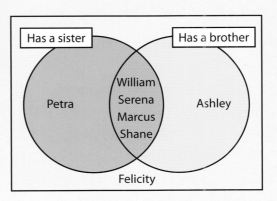

Example

Seven people have curry or chips.

Two of them have chips only.
One of them has both curry and chips.

Use a Venn diagram to find out how many had curry only.

In order to make the total 7, 4 people must have had curry only.

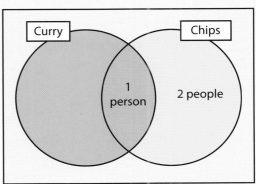

1   Work in a group of five or six with one copy of **S2.3 Resource sheet 2.1**.
    The instructions are on the resource sheet.

2   The table shows information about
    endangered animals.

    a   Show this data in a Carroll
        diagram.

        Use two properties:
        endangered or not,
        and vegetarian or not.

    b   How many animals are both
        vegetarian and endangered?

    c   How many are not vegetarian?

Animal	Endangered	Food
Asian elephant	Yes	Grass, bark branches
Giraffe	No	Leaves and twigs
Gorilla	Yes	Plants, ants and termites
Hippo	No	Grass
Lion	No	Wildebeest, zebra and other animals
Diana monkey	Yes	Fruit and insects
Rhino	Yes	Plants and grass
Plains zebra	No	Plants and grasses
Mexican wolf	Yes	Deer and other animals

3   The table shows data on animals
    that live in the rainforest.

    a   Show this data in a Venn diagram.

        Use two sets:
        'longer than 2 metres' and
        'lifespan of more than 20 years'.

    b   Which animals are over 2 metres long
        and live longer than 20 years?

    c   What fraction of the animals are
        less than 2 metres and live less
        than 20 years?

Animal	Life span	Adult length
Tiger	18 years	3 m
Poison arrow frog	12 years	2 cm
Scarlet macaw	80 years	90 cm
Boa constrictor	35 years	3.6 m
Rhino	40 years	3 m
Vampire bat	19 years	20 cm
Chimpanzee	60 years	1.2 m
Linn's sloth	32 years	70 cm
Lion tamarind	8 years	34 cm

Extension problems

4 Draw a Venn diagram to help you to answer this question.

There are 25 pupils in a class.
They all chose to go swimming or go to the cinema.
10 of them chose to do both.
7 of them chose only to go swimming.

How many chose only to go to the cinema?

5 The Venn diagram shows how many children like fishing, swimming and trampolining.

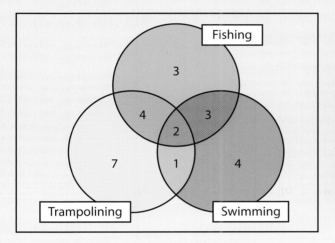

a How many children like all three sports?

b How many children are there altogether?

c How many children like swimming?

d How many children like trampolining and fishing but don't like swimming?

e How many children like fishing and swimming?

Points to remember

⊙ Venn and Carroll diagrams are sorting diagrams.

⊙ A **Carroll diagram** has rectangles for sorting the data according to whether or not it has the given properties.

⊙ A **Venn diagram** has circles:

– the data in the overlap of the circles has both properties;

– the data outside the circles has neither property.

3 Bar charts and pie charts

This lesson will help you to draw and interpret bar charts and to interpret pie charts.

Bar charts

4000 pupils were asked about their favourite activity.

The **table** and the **bar chart** show the results.

The bar chart shows that the most popular activity was going out, followed by sport and watching TV. Art and reading were the least popular.

Activity	Frequency
Watching TV	800
Sport	921
Music	565
Shopping	358
Art	256
Going out	936
Reading	164

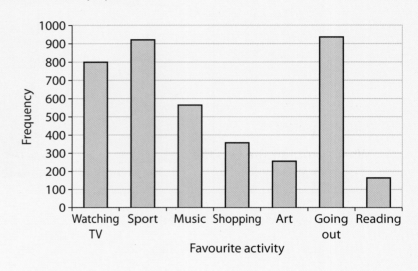

In a **bar chart**:

◉ the axes must be labelled;

◉ the scales must have labels on the lines;

◉ there should be a gap between the bars.

Pie charts

This pie chart also shows the favourite activities of the 4000 pupils.

The pink area is the largest, so going out was most popular activity.

The dark blue area is the smallest, so reading was the least popular activity.

Most of the chart is pink, purple or green. Going out, watching TV and sport are most people's favourite activities.

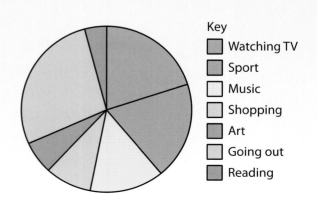

Key
- Watching TV
- Sport
- Music
- Shopping
- Art
- Going out
- Reading

You will need a ruler, large pieces of centimetre squared paper and a sharp pencil.

1. Work in a group of three.
   You each need a copy of **S2.3 Resource sheet 1.2**.
   This has the results of the class survey you did at the beginning of the unit.

   a Draw a bar chart for your group of the results of questions 1, 2 and 3.
   Each of you should draw a bar chart for a different question.

   Label the vertical axis in ones.

   On the horizontal axis, make the bars 1 cm wide with 1 cm gaps between them.

   b Write a sentence that describes what your bar chart shows.

2. Viewers were asked to vote for their favourite Saturday morning TV programme.
   The results are shown in the pie chart.

   a Which programme was the most popular?

   b Which programme was the least popular?

   c Four programmes had most of the votes. Which are they?

Key
- Live and Kicking
- Swapshop
- Going Live!
- Dick & Dom in da Bungalow
- Saturday Superstore
- Saturday Show

Data source: www.saturdaymornings.co.uk

3. This table shows the favourite TV programmes of 4000 pupils.

   a Draw a bar chart to represent the data.

   Label the vertical axis in 100s.

   Make the bars on the horizontal axis 1 cm wide with 1 cm gaps between them.

   b Write a sentence to say what the graph shows.

   Make sure you say what the favourite kinds of programme were and the least favourite.

Type of programme	Frequency
Documentary	100
Comedy	300
Drama	350
Soap	550
Quiz	650
Film	550
News	75
Travel	50
Sport	475
Entertainment	900

4 Here is a bar chart.

It shows the average number of hours of TV children of different ages watched each day.

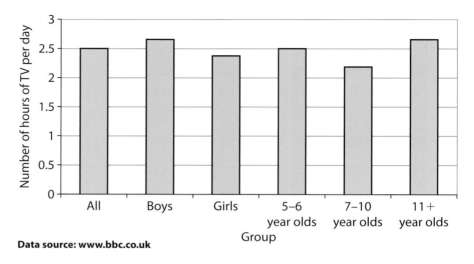

Data source: www.bbc.co.uk

a Who watched more TV, boys or girls?

b Which age group watched the most TV?

Why do you think this is? Write two different reasons.

5 100 children aged 11–16 were asked about the multimedia equipment they owned.
The results are in the table.

Item	Frequency
Own TV	88
Own DVD player	81
TV, DVD and video recorder	52
Multichannel TV	21
Own PC/laptop	47

Data source: adapted from ww.bbc.co.uk

a Draw a bar chart to represent the data.
Use a scale of 1 cm per 10 pupils on the vertical axis.
Make the bars 1 cm wide with 1 cm gaps between them.

b Write a sentence to say what the graph shows.

Points to remember

⊙ In a **bar chart**, the height of a bar shows the frequency for that category.

⊙ In a **pie chart**, the size of a 'slice of pie' shows the frequency for that category.

4 Bar-line graphs

This lesson will help you to draw and interpret bar-line graphs.

Exercise 4

Terri threw a dice 20 times. She recorded the score she got each time in a tally chart:

Score	Tally	Frequency
1	IIII	4
2	III	3
3	⅏	5
4	⅏	5
5	II	2
6	I	1

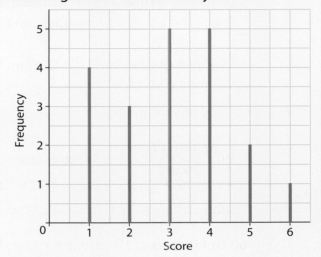

The results are shown in a bar-line graph.

It shows that some numbers came up more than others.

In a **bar-line graph**, remember that:

☺ frequency goes on the vertical axis;

☺ label the grid lines not the spaces;

☺ label the axes;

☺ space out the categories evenly on the horizontal axis.

You will need a ruler, sharp pencil and graph paper.

① Work with a partner. You need a dice.

a Copy the tally chart into one of your books.

b One of you should roll the dice ten times.
The other records the scores in the tally chart.

Swap over and roll the dice ten more times.
Record the second ten scores in the chart.

c Each of you should draw a bar-line graph
to represent your results.

Label the vertical axis in ones.
Space the bar-lines 1 cm apart on the horizontal axis.

Score	Tally	Frequency
1		
2		
3		
4		
5		
6		

2 You will need a copy of **S2.3 Resource sheet 1.2**.
This has the results of the class survey you carried out at the beginning of the unit.

a Draw a bar-line graph to represent the class results for question 4.

Label the vertical axis in twos from 0 to 16.
Space the bar-lines 1 cm apart on the horizontal axis.

b Draw a bar-line graph to represent the class results for question 5.

Label the vertical axis in twos from 0 to 16.
Space the bar-lines 1 cm apart on the horizontal axis.

3 The bar-line graph shows the spelling test results for a class of 30 pupils.

a Copy this frequency chart.

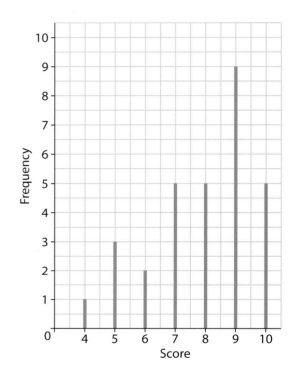

Spelling test score	Frequency
4	
5	
6	
7	
8	
9	
10	

Use the bar-line graph to help you complete it.

b What was the best mark?

c How many people got 7 marks?

d Write a sentence to say what the bar-line graph shows.

Points to remember

⊙ A **bar-line graph** shows data where the categories are numbers, such as scores in a game, that can be placed in order.

⊙ The bar-lines must be evenly spaced along the horizontal axis.

5 Mode and range

This lesson will help you to find the mode and range of a small set of data.

Exercise 5

The **range** is found by subtracting the smallest data value from the largest.

The **mode** is the most common value in the set of data.

A data set can have more than one mode.

If all the numbers are different then the data set has no mode.

Example 1

The table shows the number of children in a class born in each season of the year.

What is the mode for the birthday seasons?

Most people were born in autumn.

This makes autumn the mode.

Season	Number of people
Spring	6
Summer	5
Autumn	10
Winter	9

Example 2

The list gives the day of the month for the birthdays of the pupils in the class.

4, 6, 10, 10, 10, 23, 29, 1, 5, 28,
2, 18, 30, 14, 13, 22, 25, 16, 5, 3,
25, 14, 1, 17, 4, 26, 22, 9, 12, 28

What is the range of the numbers in the list?

The smallest number in the data set is 1.

The largest number is 30.

The range is 30 − 1 = 29.

1   You need a copy of **S2.3 Resource sheet 1.2**, which contains the results of the class survey you carried out at the beginning of the unit.

   a   Find the mode and range for the data for question 4 on the resource sheet.

   b   Find the mode and range for the data for question 5 on the resource sheet.

2 a Find the mode and range for this set of numbers.

3, 6, 7, 8, 4, 5, 6, 6, 2, 1

b Now find the mode and range for this set of numbers.

4, 7, 8, 9, 5, 6, 7, 7, 3, 2

c How can you get the second set of numbers from the first?

d How did the mode and range change when the numbers changed?

3 a Write down ten numbers between 1 and 10. Use some of the numbers more than once.

b Find the mode and range for the data set.

c Now make up a new data set by adding 5 to each of the numbers in your data set in part a.

d Find the mode and range for the new data set.

e How did the mode and range change when you added 5 to each of the numbers?

4 a Make up a data set with ten numbers that has no mode.

b Make up a data set with ten numbers that has two different modes.

c Make up a data set with ten numbers that has a mode of 3 and a range of 7.

⊙ Points to remember

- ⊙ The **mode** is the most common value in the set of data.
- ⊙ To find the **range**, subtract the smallest data value from the largest.
- ⊙ You can also find the mode and range from a diagram.

How well are you doing?

1 *2003 Progress Test level 3*

The table shows the medals that Britain won in the Olympic Games in the year 2000 and in the year 1996.

Year	Number of medals		
	Gold	**Silver**	**Bronze**
2000	11	10	7
1996	1	8	6

Copy and complete the bar chart to show the medals that were won in 1996.

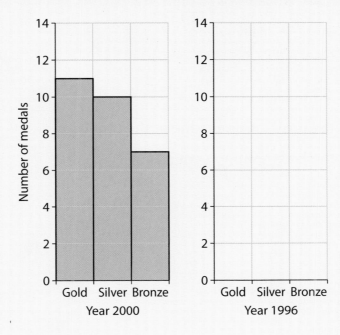

This question is about pupils in class 7Y.

The graph shows how many of these pupils were at school each day.

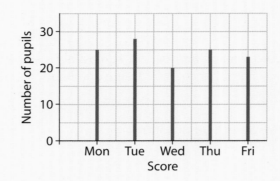

a On which days were only 25 pupils at school?

b On Tuesday all the pupils in class 7Y were at school.
   How many of these pupils were not at school on Wednesday?

③ The pie chart shows the ages of pupils in a youth club.

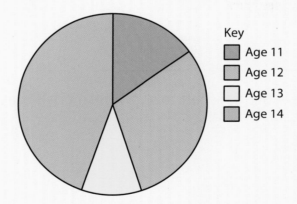

Key
■ Age 11
■ Age 12
□ Age 13
■ Age 14

a What was the most common age of the pupils?

b What was the least common age?

Measures

This unit will help you to:

- choose and use standard metric units for length, mass and capacity;
- use decimals to record measurements;
- recognise some imperial units;
- convert between units of measurement;
- compare readings on different scales;
- work out time intervals using am, pm and the 24-hour clock;
- use timetables.

1 Converting units

This lesson will help you to convert between units of measurement in the same system.

 Did you know that...?

In the 1700s, many different units of measurement were used around the world.

For example, lengths could be measured in feet, inches, miles, spans, cubits, hands, furlongs, palms, rods, chains, leagues, and more!

This made it difficult to buy and sell things in different countries.

In 1790, the French introduced the **metric system**.

This is now used in nearly every country in the world except the United States.

Stamp from Pakistan
showing measuring equipment

To change one metric unit to another you need to know these relationships.

Length
10 mm = 1 cm
100 cm = 1 m
1000 mm = 1 m
1000 m = 1 km

Weight
1000 g = 1 kg

Capacity/volume
1000 ml = 1 litre

For example, to convert lengths, you can use this diagram:

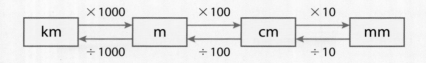

○ When you change from a unit to a *larger* unit, you **divide**.

○ When you change from a unit to a *smaller* unit, you **multiply**.

Example

Change 3.17 litres to millilitres.

In every litre there are 1000 millilitres.

So 3.17 litres = 3.17 × 1000 ml = 3170 ml

You may **use your calculator**.

① Play **Matching measurements** with a partner.
You will need a calculator and the cards cut out from **G2.4 Resource sheet 1.1**.

○ Shuffle the cards. Spread them out face up on the table.

○ Sort the cards into matching pairs of equivalent quantities.
Use the tables at the top of this page to help you.

○ Use a calculator to check your answers.

② Change to metres.

a 430 cm   b 68 cm   c 3 cm

Change to centimetres.

d 5.6 m   e 69 m   f 0.9 m

3 Change to litres.

    a 3400 ml   **b** 451 ml   **c** 56 ml

Change to millilitres.

    d 0.4 litres   **e** 3.06 litres   **f** 0.552 litres

4 Change to grams.

    a 12.8 kg   **b** 0.87 kg   **c** 0.3 kg

Change to kilograms.

    d 5430 g   **e** 897 g   **f** 64 g

5 **a** Eliza is making bread.
      She needs 0.55 kg of flour.
      She has already put 240 g in the mixing bowl.
      How much more flour does she need?

    b Eliza uses $\frac{1}{2}$ litre of water to make the bread.
      How many millilitres is this?

    c Eliza's table is 38 cm wide and 1.2 m long.
      How long is the perimeter?
      Give your answer in metres.

    d Flour comes in $\frac{3}{4}$ kilogram bags.
      Eliza bought 5 bags.
      How many grams of flour did she buy in total?

6 A glass of milkshake uses 230 ml milk.

    a David has a $\frac{1}{2}$ litre carton of milk.
      He pours out the milk to make one milkshake.
      How many millilitres of milk are left in the carton?

    b How many millilitres of milk do you need for four milkshakes?

    c How many milkshakes can you make from 3 litres of milk?

    d A bottle of strawberry juice contains 1 litre.
      David uses $\frac{1}{10}$ of it to make milkshakes.
      How many millilitres of the juice are left?

Points to remember

- To change a unit to a *larger* unit, you **divide.**
- To change a unit to a *smaller* unit, you **multiply**.
- When an answer is a measurement, include the units.

2 Reading scales

This lesson will help you to compare numbers on different scales.

When you read a scale, you have to work out what each interval on the scale represents.

If the pointer points between two marks on the scale, you have to estimate the reading.

The pointer on this scale shows a reading of about 0.45.

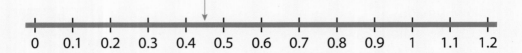

The pointer on this scale shows a reading of about 790.

1   You will need a copy of **G2.4 Resource sheet 2.1**. Answer the questions on the sheet.

2   Write the number shown by each scale.

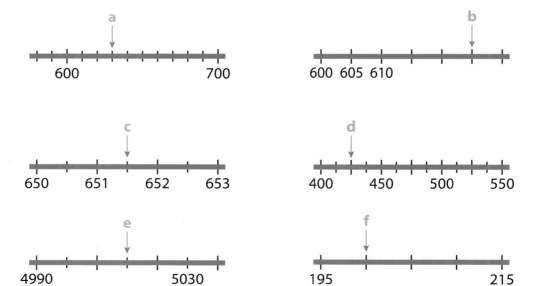

3 **a** Estimate the length of each piece of string.

A

| 0 | 0.1 | 0.2 | 0.3 | 0.4 | 0.5 m |

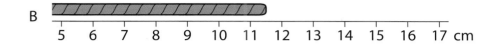

B

5   6   7   8   9   10   11   12   13   14   15   16   17 cm

b Which piece of string is longer, A or B?

4 **a** Estimate the reading on each of these kitchen scales.

b Which bag is heavier, A or B?

5 **a** Estimate the quantity of liquid in each of these containers.

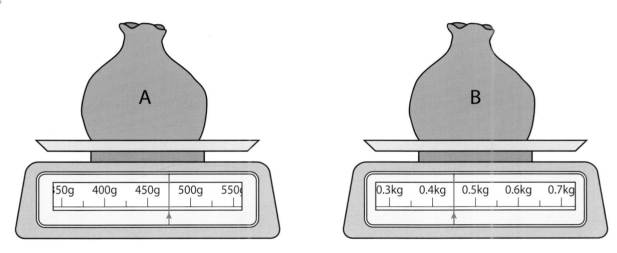

A   B

b Which container contains more liquid, A or B?

6 Here are two thermometers.
They show different temperatures.
What is the difference between the
two temperatures?

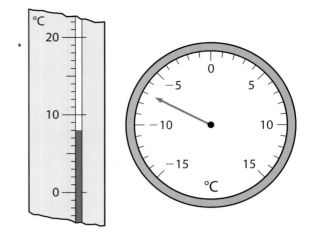

Extension problem

7 The diagram shows a scale marked in litres and in gallons.

a Estimate the volume in litres when the pointer is at 4 gallons.

b Estimate the volume in litres when the pointer is at $1\frac{1}{2}$ gallons.

c Estimate the volume in gallons when the pointer is at 10 litres.

d Estimate the volume in gallons when the pointer is at 4 litres.

Litres   Gallons

Points to remember

- To read a scale, first decide what each interval represents.
- Work out the values of the marks close to the pointer.
- If the pointer lies between two marks, estimate the reading between them.
- When you calculate, make sure the measurements are in the same units.
- Remember to include the units in your answer.

3 Estimating and measuring

This lesson will help you to estimate and measure lengths, weights and volumes.

 Did you know that…?

The tallest tower in the world in 2007 was Taipei 101. It is 509 metres tall.

Taipei 101 is the world's tallest building. It was built in 2004 and is 509 m high.

The **Empire State Building** in New York was built in 1931. It is 320 m high.

The **Eiffel tower** in Paris was built in 1889. Its height is 324 m.

The tallest tower in the UK is **Canary Wharf**. It is 235 metres tall.

Blackpool Tower is 62 metres tall.

Exercise 3

Units for length are: millimetres (mm), centimetres (cm), metres (m), kilometres (km).

Units for weight are: grams (g), kilograms (kg).

Units for capacity/volume are: millilitres (ml), litres (l).

Work in a group of four.
Each person needs a copy of **G2.4 Resource sheet 3.1**.

Each of you should fill in the sheet separately.

For each row on the sheet:

- Read the description and find a suitable object.
- Estimate the measurement for the object.
  Remember to include units for your answer.
- Measure the object.
  You will need to choose which measuring tool to use.
- Remember to include the units when you write your estimates and measurements.

Points to remember

- Metres, kilograms and litres are examples of **metric units**.
- Gallons, pints and miles are examples of **imperial units**.
- When an answer is a measurement include the units.

4 Time intervals

This lesson will help you to use the 24-hour clock and to calculate time intervals.

Did you know that...?

In the old days, sundials were used to tell the time.

Sundials have existed for 4000 years. Clocks and watches replaced them in the 18th century.

Early clocks were often unreliable. People still depended on sundials for the true time.

Exercise 4

This is a clock that shows 24 hours.

8:00 pm is 20:00 in 24-hour clock time.

24-hour clock times don't need am or pm.
The hours from 00 to 11 are in the morning.
The hours from 12 up to 23 are in the afternoon or evening.

21:15 is 9:15 pm.   08:34 is 8:34 am.

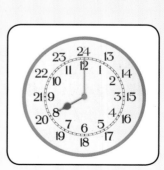

- To get 24-hour clock times after midday, add 12 to the number of hours.
- To get 12-hour from 24-hour clock times, subtract 12 from the number of hours.

Use a **time line** to help with time calculations.

Example

A train leaves London Paddington at 20:35 and arrives in Exeter at 23:43.
How long did the journey take?

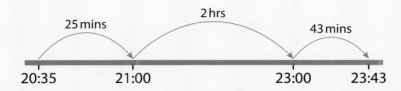

The journey time is the total of 25 minutes, 2 hours and 43 minutes.

25 minutes and 43 minutes is 68 minutes or 1 hour and 8 minutes,

So the total journey time is 2 hours plus 1 hour and 8 minutes, which is 3 hours 8 minutes.

1 Write these times as 24-hour clock times.

a 6 o'clock in the morning
b quarter past 9 in the evening
c 4 o'clock in the afternoon
d 12 minutes past midnight
e quarter to 11 in the morning
f 17 minutes past 8 in the evening
g 25 past 9 in the morning
h 12 minutes to midnight

2 Write these times using am and pm.

a 21:00
b 07:00
c 19:20
d 23:21
e 00:25
f 04:40
g 12:29
h 21:55

3 The bus from Sunderland to Newcastle leaves at 07:35.
It arrives at 08:13.
How long does the journey take?

4 A journey takes 25 minutes on the bus,
3 hours 30 minutes on the train
and then 10 minutes walking.
How long is the journey in total?

5   A train leaves Edinburgh at 09:10.
    It arrives in London at 14:45.
    How long does the journey take?

Write your answers to the rest of the questions in 24-hour clock time.

6   Lessons are 50 minutes long.
    The first lesson of the school day finishes at 09:25.
    At what time does it start?

7   Fiona wants to watch a film.
    The film starts at 19:15 and lasts 1 hour and 35 minutes.
    At what time does it finish?

8   Dean is cooking a casserole. It needs to be ready at 19:15.
    It takes 3 hours and 45 minutes to cook.
    What time does it need to go in the oven?

Extension problem

9   The record for cycling from Land's End to John O'Groats is held by Andy Wilkinson.

It took him 41 hours 4 minutes 22 seconds on his tricycle.
Assume that Andy left Land's End at 09:00 on a Monday and didn't stop.
When did he reach John O'Groats?

Points to remember

- 00:00 is **midnight**. 12:00 is **midday** or **noon**.
- On the 24-hour clock, the hours 00, 01, 02, …, 11 are in the morning; the hours 12, 13, 14, …, 23 are in the afternoon or evening.
- To change 24-hour to 12-hour clock times, subtract 12 from the hours.
- A time line can help with time calculations.

5 Timetables

This lesson will help you to use timetables.

 Did you know that...?

George Bradshaw published the world's first railway timetables in 1839.
His timetables were used for more than 100 years.

Exercise 5

A **timetable** tells you the times when things will happen.

This is part of the timetable for the weekday Central Trains service from Liverpool to Nottingham.
Each column is a separate journey.

Liverpool Lime Street	06:47	07:47	08:52	09:52	10:52
Warrington	07:14	08:16	09:17	10:17	11:17
Manchester Piccadilly	07:43	08:42	09:42	10:42	11:42
Stockport	07:54	08:53	09:53	10:55	11:55
Sheffield	08:38	09:38	10:38	11:38	12:38
Chesterfield	08:52	09:53	10:53	11:53	12:53
Nottingham	09:35	10:31	11:32	12:34	13:31

The first train to leave Liverpool Lime Street leaves at 06:47.
This train arrives in Nottingham at 09:35.

Example

Tara wants go from Manchester Piccadilly and get to Nottingham by 1:00 pm.

a   Which train should she catch?

The 10:42 from Manchester Piccadilly, which arrives in Nottingham at 12:34.

b   How long will her journey take?

From 10:42 to 11:00 is 18 minutes. From 11:00 to 12:34 is 1 hour 34 minutes.

The total journey time is 1 hour 34 minutes + 18 minutes = 1 hour 52 minutes.

① Here are the start and finish times of some friends doing a sponsored bike ride.

	Start time	Finish time
Hannah	14:30	15:55
Alex	14:35	16:05
Simon	14:40	16:08
Darren	14:45	16:05

How much longer did Claire take than Tim?

② This is part of the timetable for the train service from Lincoln to Burton Joyce.

Lincoln Central	09:23	10:36	11:43	12:31	13:35
Hykeham	09:31	10:44		12:39	13:43
Newark Castle	09:54	11:03	12:05	12:58	14:03
Rolleston	10:01	11:10		13:05	
Thurgarton	10:10			13:13	
Lowdham	10:14	11:17		13:17	
Burton Joyce	10:18	11:21	12:20	13:21	14:18

a On Monday, Fraser gets the 09:23 train from Lincoln Central.
   At what time does he arrive at Burton Joyce?

b How long does Monday's journey take him?

c On Tuesday, Fraser gets the 10:36 train from Lincoln Central to Burton Joyce.
   How long does this journey take him?

d Why do you think Tuesday's journey takes him a different length of time?

e On Wednesday, Fraser arrives at Lincoln Central station at 12:15.
   What is the next train he can catch to Burton Joyce?

f At what time will he arrive at Burton Joyce?

g How long is the fastest journey from Lincoln Central to Burton Joyce?

3 You can go from Southampton to Cowes on the Isle of Wight by hydrofoil or ferry.

The hydrofoil runs every half hour from 05:45 to 22:45.

The ferry runs every hour from 01:00 to 23:00.

Depart	Arrive
05:45	06:08
then every half hour until	
20:45	21:08

Depart	Arrive
01:00	01:55
then every half hour until	
23:00	23:55

a How long does the hydrofoil journey take?

b At what time will the 06:15 hydrofoil arrive at Cowes?

c How long does the ferry journey take?

d How much longer does the ferry journey take than the hydrofoil?

e Zoe has just missed the 09:45 hydrofoil.
  Should she catch the 10:00 ferry or wait for the 10:15 hydrofoil? Why?

4 This is part of a bus timetable on Guernsey.

Town (depart)	14:55	15:55	16:12	16:55
The Banks	14:59	15:59	16:14	16:59
Admiral Park	15:01	16:01	16:16	17:01
Collings Road	15:08	16:08	16:23	17:08
Footes Lane	15:10	16:10	16:25	17:10
Rohais	15:12	16:12	16:27	17:12
Top of Grange	15:15	16:15	16:30	17:15
Town (arrive)	15:22	16:22	16:37	17:22

a How long does the bus take from Admiral Park to Collings Road?

b The bus route is circular.
  How long does it take to do the whole circuit?

c Amy catches the 14:59 bus at The Banks.
  How long will it take her to get to Rohais?

d Paul arrives at the bus stop at The Banks at 4:45 pm.
  How long will he have to wait for the next bus?

e Marie wants to get to Footes Lane by 4:30 pm.
  At what time will she need to catch a bus from the Town?

5 The Isle of Wight Steam Railway has one train.
It runs from Smallbrook Junction to Wootton and back again on the single line

Smallbrook Junction   Ashey   Havenstreet   Wootton

Here are the timetables.

Smallbrook Junction	Depart		11.02	12.13	13.21		15.11	16.19
Havenstreet	Arrive		11.14	12.25	13.33		15.23	16.31
	Depart		11.17	12.28		14.17	15.26	
Wootton	Arrive		11.23	12.34		14.23	15.32	

Wootton	Depart		11.31	12.42		14.31	15.40
Havenstreet	Arrive		11.37	13.48		14.37	15.46
	Depart	10.35	11.51	12.59		14.51	15.59
Smallbrook Junction	Arrive	10.48	12.03	13.11		15.03	16.11

a Where does the train start from every morning?

b Matt catches the 12:13 from Smallbrook Junction.
What time does he arrive at Wootton?

c How long does Matt's journey take?

d Mary and her family are planning a day out in Wootton.
They want to go by train from Havenstreet.
What is the longest possible time that they can spend in Wootton?
Give the times of the trains they will need to catch.

Points to remember

⊙ Timetables often use the 24-hour clock.

⊙ Each column or row is a separate journey.

⊙ A blank space in a timetable means that there is no stop at that place.

How well are you doing?

Can you:

- use standard metric units for length, mass and capacity?
- use decimals to record measurements?
- recognise some imperial units?
- convert between units of measurement?
- compare readings on different scales?
- work out time intervals using am, pm and the 24-hour clock?
- use timetables?

1 *2003 KS2 level 4*

Write these lengths in order,
starting with the shortest.

$\frac{1}{2}$ m

3.5 cm

25 mm

20 cm

2 *2003 KS2 level 4*

Katie's glass holds a quarter of a litre when it is full.
She fills it nearly to the top with juice.
What is the approximate amount of juice she puts in the glass?

4 millilitres   20 millilitres   120 millilitres   220 millilitres   420 millilitres

3 *2003 KS2 level 4*

Here are some apples.
What is their total weight?

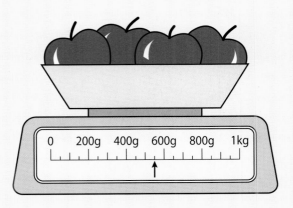

2003 level 3

a My wall clock shows this time.

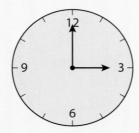

Which two of the digital clocks below could be showing the same time as my wall clock?

A

`03:00`

B

`13:00`

C

`14:00`

D

`15:00`

E

`16:00`

b Early in the morning my wall clock shows this time.

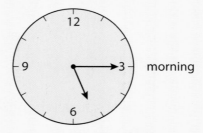

morning

My digital clock shows the same time as my wall clock.
Write what time my digital clock is showing.

c In the afternoon my wall clock shows this time.

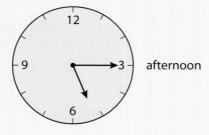

afternoon

My digital clock is a 24-hour clock.
Now what time is my digital clock showing?

5 *2007 Key Stage 2 level 3*

Jamie makes a time line of part of his day.

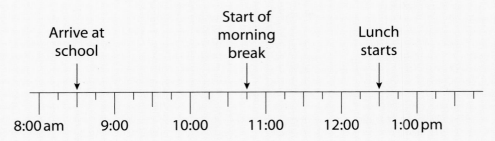

a What time does Jamie's morning break start?

b Lunch lasts for three-quarters of an hour.

What time does lunch finish?

6 *2005 Key Stage 2 level 3*

These are the radio programmes one morning.

7:00	Music show
7:55	Weather report
8:00	News
8:15	Travel news
8:25	Sport
8:45	Holiday programme

a Josh turns the radio on at 7:25 am.

How many minutes does he have to wait for the Weather report?

b The Holiday programme lasts for 40 minutes.

At what time does the Holiday programme finish?

7 *1998 Key Stage 2 level 4*

These are the start and finish times on a video cassette recorder.

START	**14:45**
FINISH	**17:25**

For how long was the video recording?

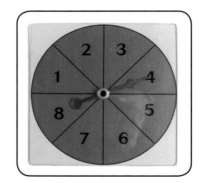

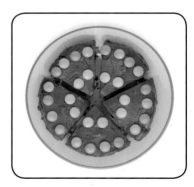

N 2.6

Fractions, percentages and direct proportion

This unit will help you to:

- compare two fractions and say which one is bigger;
- add and subtract simple fractions;
- find two fractions that add up to 1;
- find simple fractions and percentages of amounts;
- scale numbers up or down;
- solve problems involving simple ideas of ratio and proportion.

1 Comparing fractions

This lesson will help you to compare fractions.

Exercise 1

These two rectangles are the same size.

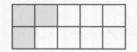

$\frac{3}{10}$ of this rectangle is shaded.

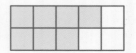

$\frac{7}{10}$ of this rectangle is shaded.

The second rectangle has more parts shaded than the first rectangle.

This shows that $\frac{7}{10}$ is bigger than $\frac{3}{10}$.

To put fractions with the same denominator in order, compare the numerators.

① Write each fraction as simply as you can.

  a $\frac{3}{12}$ b $\frac{2}{8}$ c $\frac{5}{15}$ d $\frac{9}{12}$ e $\frac{8}{10}$ f $\frac{4}{6}$

② What fraction is shaded? Write each answer as simply as you can.

a 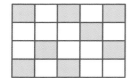   b   c

d   e

③ Write the fraction that is bigger.

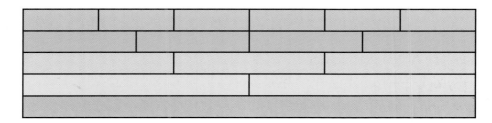

  a $\frac{1}{2}$ or $\frac{1}{3}$ b $\frac{1}{6}$ or $\frac{1}{4}$ c $\frac{1}{3}$ or $\frac{1}{4}$

  d $\frac{2}{3}$ or $\frac{3}{4}$ e $\frac{5}{6}$ or $\frac{3}{4}$ f $\frac{1}{2}$ or $\frac{2}{3}$

④ Play **Comparing fractions** with a partner. You need two dice.

Rules

○ The first player rolls the two dice.
   If the two numbers are the same, roll again.

○ If the two numbers are different, write down a fraction.
   Use the smaller number as the numerator and the larger as the denominator.

○ The second player now rolls the two dice and makes a fraction in the same way.

○ Compare your two fractions. If they are the same size, you both score a point.
   If they are a different size, the player with the bigger fraction scores a point.

○ The winner is the first player to get 8 points.

(5) Work with a partner.
You need **N2.6 Resource sheet 1.1** and some scissors.

   a Shade the fractions of the circles.

   b Cut out all the fractions and arrange them in order of size.

(6) a Write three fractions that are equivalent to $\frac{1}{2}$.

   b Write three fractions that are equivalent to $\frac{1}{3}$.

   c Write three fractions that are equivalent to $\frac{3}{4}$.

Extension problems

(7) Write each fraction as simply as you can.

   a $\frac{15}{20}$ b $\frac{16}{32}$ c $\frac{30}{100}$ d $\frac{12}{18}$ e $\frac{10}{25}$ f $\frac{18}{20}$

(8) Ali and Bob have identical chocolate bars.

Ali eats $\frac{3}{4}$ of his chocolate bar.

Bob eats $\frac{7}{8}$ of his chocolate bar.

Who eats more chocolate?
Give a reason for your answer.

Points to remember

⊙ To find an **equivalent fraction**, multiply or divide the numerator and the denominator by the same number.

⊙ Dividing the numerator and the denominator by the same number is **cancelling** or **simplifying** the fraction.

⊙ Use diagrams to **compare fractions**, or change them to equivalent fractions with the same denominator.

2 Fractions, decimals and percentages

This lesson will help you to find equivalent fractions, decimals and percentages.

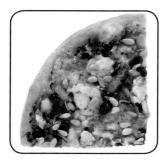 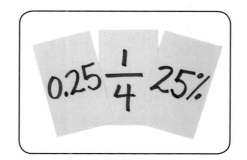 

Exercise 2

Per cent means 'out of 100'. 35 per cent is written as 35%.

35 per cent means 35 out of 100. This is $\frac{35}{100}$ as a fraction and 0.35 as a decimal.

Learn these percentage, fraction and decimal equivalents.

Percentage	100%	50%	25%	75%	10%	20%	1%
Fraction	$\frac{100}{100}=1$	$\frac{50}{100}=\frac{1}{2}$	$\frac{25}{100}=\frac{1}{4}$	$\frac{75}{100}=\frac{3}{4}$	$\frac{10}{100}=\frac{1}{10}$	$\frac{20}{100}=\frac{1}{5}$	$\frac{1}{100}$
Decimal	1	0.5	0.25	0.75	0.1	0.2	0.01

1. Write each percentage as a fraction.

   a 59%   b 7%   c 1%   d 21%

2. Write each percentage as a fraction in its simplest form.

   a 75%   b 25%   c 30%   d 90%

   e 50%   f 2%   g 15%   h 16%

3. Give your answers in their simplest form.

   a 25% of children walk to school.
   What fraction is this?

   b 40% of the houses on a street have a wooden front door.
   What fraction is this?

   c 60% of the children at a playgroup are boys.
   What fraction is this?

4   **a**   30% of the ices sold in a shop have nuts on.
What fraction is this?

    b   15% of the ices sold in a shop are cones.
What fraction is this?

    c   20% of the pupils in a class have an ice cream at lunchtime.
What fraction is this?

5   Write each percentage as a decimal.

    a   23%   **b**   95%   **c**   7%   **d**   25%

    e   60%   **f**   3%   **g**   40%   **h**   57%

6   Write each decimal as a percentage.

    a   0.75   **b**   0.23   **c**   0.4   **d**   0.08

    e   0.3   **f**   0.01   **g**   0.05   **h**   1.25

7   Play **Matching pairs** with a partner.
You need cards made from **N2.6 Resource sheet 2.1**.

    Rules

    ◉   Shuffle the cards. Put them face down on the table.

    ◉   Take turns to turn over two cards.

    ◉   If the cards match, keep them and have another turn.

    ◉   If the cards are not equivalent, turn them back face down.
It is then the other player's turn.

    ◉   The winner is the player with more pairs when all the cards are won.

Extension problem

8   Amrita has done three tests.
She wants to know what her best subject is.
Change Amrita's marks to percentages.
Write the subjects in order, with her best subject first.

English: $\frac{21}{25}$ Maths: $\frac{17}{20}$ Science: $\frac{41}{50}$

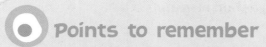

Points to remember

- Percentage means 'per hundred', or 'in every hundred'.
- A percentage like 37% can be written as $\frac{37}{100}$ or as 0.37.
- One half is 50%, $\frac{1}{2}$ or 0.5.
- One quarter is 25%, $\frac{1}{4}$ or 0.25.
- One tenth is 10%, $\frac{1}{10}$ or 0.1.
- From this, you can work out that 70% is $\frac{7}{10}$ or 0.7.

3 Percentages of quantities

This lesson will help you to work out percentages of amounts.

Exercise 3

25% is the same as $\frac{1}{4}$.
To find 25%, find half of 50%.

75% is the same as $\frac{3}{4}$.
To find 75%, add 50% and 25%.

10% is the same as $\frac{1}{10}$.
To find 10%, divide by 10.

Example

Find 5% of £120.

10% of £120 is £120 ÷ 10 = £12

5% is half of 10%.
So 5% of £120 is £12 ÷ 2 = £6

1 What percentage of each shape is shaded?

a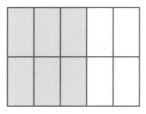

b

2 Draw a grid like this one.

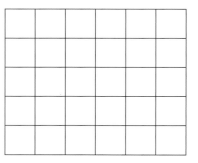

a Colour 10% of the squares red.

b Colour 20% of the squares blue.

c Colour 30% of the squares green.

d What percentage of the squares are not coloured?

3 Ella counted the cars in a car park.

Colour of car	Tally
Silver	IIII IIII IIII IIII
White	IIII IIII I
Black	IIII IIII II
Other	IIII II

a How many cars were in the car park?

b What percentage of the cars were silver?

c What percentage of the cars were white?

d What percentage of the cars were black?

e What percentage of the cars were other colours?

4 200 people voted for their three favourite sports.

50 people voted for football.

a What percentage of the people voted for football?

b What fraction of the people voted for football?

100 people voted for jogging.

c What percentage of the people voted for jogging?

d What fraction of the people voted for jogging?

Three quarters of the people voted for swimming.

e What percentage of the people voted for swimming?

f How many people voted for swimming?

20% of the people voted for table tennis.

g What fraction of the people voted for table tennis?

h How many people voted for table tennis?

One tenth of the people voted for badminton.

i What percentage of the people voted for badminton?

j How many people voted for badminton?

5 Work these out.

a 50% of £50

b 10% of 90 cm

c 25% of 80 g

d 20% of £250

e 5% of 100 km

f 75% of 10 m

g 1% of 600 ml

h 40% of 90p

i 60% of 50 kg

j 30% of 20 l

k 90% of £10

l 2% of 500 g

6 Play **Percentage jackpot** with a partner.
You need a dice.

This table shows you what each roll of the dice is worth.

Dice number	1	2	3	4	5	6
Percentage score	5%	10%	15%	20%	25%	30%

Rules

- Take turns to roll the dice. Find that percentage of £30.
  Add this to your bank.
- The winner is the player with the most in the bank after four turns each.
- Play again. This time find percentages of £45.

Extension problem

7 a Would you rather win 50% of £100 or 20% of £500?
Explain your answer.

   b Would it be cheaper to pay 75% of £200 or 40% of £400 for a holiday?
Explain your answer.

   c Would you rather be chased by 25% of 200 bees or 15% of 400 bees?
Explain your answer.

 Points to remember

- To find 10%, divide by 10.
- To find 20%, multiply 10% by 2; to find 30%, multiply 10% by 3, and so on.
- If there is no quick method, first find 1%, then multiply by the percentage.
- Always include any units in the answer.

4 Working with fractions

This lesson will help you to calculate with fractions.

Exercise 4

Here $\frac{1}{4}$ of the strip of 12 squares is coloured.

Now an extra $\frac{1}{3}$ of the strip is coloured.

Altogether, 7 squares or $\frac{7}{12}$ of the strip is coloured, so $\frac{1}{4} + \frac{1}{3} = \frac{7}{12}$.

To find $\frac{2}{3}$ of a quantity, first divide by 3, then multiply the result by 2.

Example

Find $\frac{2}{3}$ of 36 kilograms.

$36 \div 3 = 12$, so $\frac{1}{3}$ of 36 kg is 12 kg.

$12 \times 2 = 24$, so $\frac{2}{3}$ of 36 kg is 24 kg.

1   Work these out. Use a strip of 12 squares to help you.

    a $\frac{1}{2} + \frac{1}{3}$ **b** $\frac{1}{4} + \frac{2}{3}$ **c** $\frac{1}{6} + \frac{1}{3}$

    d $\frac{1}{2} - \frac{1}{3}$ **e** $\frac{2}{3} - \frac{1}{4}$ **f** $\frac{1}{3} - \frac{1}{12}$

2   Work these out. Use a strip of 10 squares if you wish.

    a $\frac{1}{2} + \frac{1}{5}$ **b** $\frac{2}{5} + \frac{3}{10}$ **c** $\frac{1}{10} + \frac{3}{5}$

    d $\frac{7}{10} - \frac{2}{5}$ **e** $\frac{3}{5} - \frac{1}{2}$ **f** $\frac{4}{5} - \frac{1}{10}$

(3) Play **Fractions** with a partner.
You need two dice.

Rules

○ Take turns to roll the two dice.
If the two numbers are the same, roll again.

○ Write a fraction, with the smaller number as numerator and the larger as denominator.

○ Work out that fraction of £36.
The other player checks the answer.

○ Have five turns each, then add up your total score.

○ The winner is the player with the greatest total score.

If you play a second game, work out fractions of £21.

(4) What fraction of an hour is each of these?

   a 15 minutes   b 10 minutes   c 40 minutes

(5) What fraction of £1 is each of these?

   a 50p   b 5p   c 20p

(6) Work these out.

   a $\frac{2}{3}$ of 45   b $\frac{3}{4}$ of 60   c $\frac{4}{5}$ of 55

   d $\frac{3}{10}$ of £70   e $\frac{2}{5}$ of 50 litres   f $\frac{3}{8}$ of 32 grams

   g $\frac{5}{9}$ of 18 kilograms   h $\frac{7}{10}$ of 50 seconds   i $\frac{5}{6}$ of 300 millilitres

(7) a Leroy gets £32 pocket money each month. He saves of $\frac{3}{4}$ of it.
      How many pounds does he save?

   b A can of fruit drink contains 350 millilitres. Sara drinks $\frac{2}{5}$ of it.
      How many millilitres of drink are left in the can?

   c A packet of rice contains 450 grams.
      Amanda uses $\frac{2}{3}$ of the flour to make a cake.
      How many grams of flour does she use?

Extension problem

8

a There are 600 seats on a jumbo jet.

$\frac{1}{20}$ of the seats are first class.

$\frac{1}{10}$ of the seats are business class.

The rest of the seats are economy class.

How many economy class seats are there?

b There are 600 passengers on a jumbo jet.

$\frac{3}{5}$ of them are men and $\frac{3}{10}$ are women.

The rest are children.

How many children are on the jumbo jet?

⊙ Points to remember

- ⊙ You can add or subtract fractions if they have the same denominator.
- ⊙ To add or subtract fractions with different denominators, change them to the same denominator.
- ⊙ Find fractions of numbers by dividing, e.g. to find one third, divide by 3.
- ⊙ To find three fifths, find one fifth then multiply by 3.

---

5 Introducing ratio and proportion

This lesson will help you to solve problems involving ratio and proportion.

Exercise 5

Look at these beads. Here are some statements about them.

- ☺ 1 in every 3 beads is red and 2 in every 3 beads are blue, so:
  - the **proportion** of red beads is $\frac{1}{3}$;
  - the **proportion** of blue beads is $\frac{2}{3}$.
- ☺ There is 1 red bead for every 2 blue beads, so:
  - the **ratio** of red beads to blue beads is 1 : 2.

A ratio can be simplified in the same way as a fraction, by dividing each side by the same number.

For example, the ratio of 5 : 10 is equivalent to a ratio of 1 : 2.

① One in every four of these squares is red.

Copy and complete these statements.

a For every red square, there are … blue squares.

b … in every 8 squares are red.

c … in every 16 squares are red.

d 3 in every … squares are red.

e 10 in every … squares are red.

f The number of blue squares is … the number of red squares.

g The proportion of red squares is … of the total number of squares.

h The ratio of red squares to blue squares is … to …

② Copy and complete the table below.

Red squares	Blue squares	Total
1	3	4
2	6	8
3	…	…
6	…	…
…	30	…

③ Simplify each of these ratios.

a 4 : 8   b 3 : 9   c 9 : 12

d 8 : 10   e 4 : 14   f 60 : 100

g 10 : 15   h 25 : 30   i 35 : 42

4 **a** Write down the ratio of the red to white parts of each of these sticks.
Write each ratio in its simplest form.

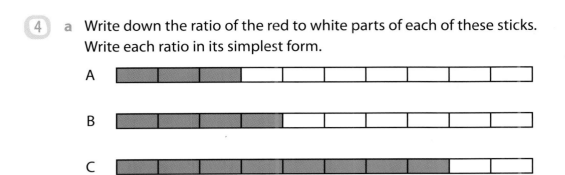

A

B

C

D

b For each stick, what fraction of the whole stick is the red part?
Write your answer as a fraction.

5 There are 100 sweets with coloured wrappers in a jar.

40 are red; 20 are green; 15 are blue; the rest are purple.

Write down each of these ratios in its simplest form.

a red sweets : blue sweets

b blue sweets : green sweets

c green sweets : purple sweets

d red sweets : purple sweets

e What fraction of the total number of sweets are the green sweets?
Write your answer as a percentage.

f What fraction of the total number of sweets are the red sweets?
Write your answer as a percentage.

Points to remember

⊙ 2 in every 3 of these beads is blue.
The **proportion** or **fraction** of blue beads is $\frac{2}{3}$.

⊙ There is 1 red bead for every 2 blue beads.
The **ratio** of red beads to blue beads is 1 : 2.

⊙ To simplify a ratio, divide each side by the same number.
For example, 5 : 10 is equivalent to 1 : 2.

6 Scaling up and down

This lesson will help you to scale numbers up and down and solve simple problems involving ideas of ratio and proportion.

Did you know that...?

One of the oldest books on mathematics was written in China over 2000 years ago.
It is called *Nine Chapters on the Mathematical Art*.

The second chapter is about exchanging grains, beans and seeds.
The book shows how to use proportions and percentages to do this.

China's famous terracotta army dates from the same time, 200 BC.
Life-sized soldiers made from clay surround the tomb of emperor Qin Shihuang.

Exercise 6

If 1 pencil costs 15p, then:

    2 pencils cost 30p (15p × 2)
    3 pencils cost 45p (15p × 3)
    4 pencils cost 60p (15p × 4) and so on.

The cost depends on the number of pencils.
As the number of pencils increases, the cost increases.

Example 1

5 buns cost £1.50.
What is the cost of 7 buns?

Work out the cost of 1 bun by dividing the cost of 5 buns by 5.

£1.50 ÷ 5 = 30p

Work out the cost of 7 buns by multiplying the cost of one bun by 7.

30p × 7 = 210p or £2.10

Example 2

Here is a recipe for carrot soup for 4 people.

Carrot soup

200 g carrots
2 onions
40 g butter
300 ml stock

Write the recipe for carrot soup for 12 people.

12 people need 3 times as much soup as 4 people.
So multiply each amount by 3.

Soup for 12 people needs 600 g carrots, 6 onions, 120 g butter and 900 ml stock.

1 One large cake costs £5.85.

   a How much do 6 large cakes cost?

   b How many large cakes can you buy for £46.80?

2 A burger costs 89p.

   a How many burgers can you buy for £13.35?

   b What do 12 burgers cost?

3 One box holds 35 DVDs.

   a How many boxes do you need to hold 420 DVDs?

   b How many DVDs are there in 7 full boxes?

4 One euro is worth 62p.

   a How many pounds will I get for 31 euros?

   b How many euros will I get for £12.40?

5   a 4 small cakes cost £1.80. How much do 24 small cakes cost?

   b 12 pens cost £9.60. How much do 4 pens cost?

   c 3 bars of soap cost £1.95. What is the cost of 18 bars of soap?

   d I can buy 28 packets of crisps for £9.80. What must I pay for 4 packets of crisps?

   e 6 eggs cost 70p. How much do 30 eggs cost?

6 Here are the ingredients to make 4 pancakes.

4 pancakes

100 g flour
140 ml of milk
2 small eggs

a What ingredients are needed to make 12 pancakes?

b What ingredients are needed to make 6 pancakes?

c How many pancakes could you make with 1 kg flour?

d How many pancakes could you make with 900 ml milk?

Points to remember

- In **scaling** problems think carefully about whether to scale up by multiplying or scale down by dividing.
- In scaling problems it can help to write a statement about one thing.
- Always write down the calculation that you do to show your working.

How well are you doing?

Fractions, percentages, ratio and proportion (no calculator)

1 *2002 Progress Test level 3*

On a school trip, one teacher must go with every 20 pupils.

a Three teachers go on a school trip.
What is the greatest number of pupils they can take with them?

b The table below shows how many pupils go on three school trips.
Copy and complete the table to show the least number of teachers that must go with each school trip.

Number of pupils	Number of teachers
100	
106	
197	

2 *2005 Progress Test level 3*

a Which of the shapes below is shaded $\frac{3}{4}$ red?

A 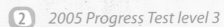   B   C

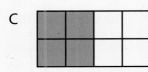

D   E   F

 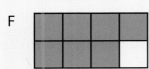

b Amy says: | $\frac{1}{2}$ of 20 is bigger than $\frac{1}{4}$ of 40 |

Is she correct? Write **Yes** or **No**.
Explain how you know.

3 *2006 Progress Test level 4*

Copy and fill in the missing numbers.

a $\frac{1}{5}$ of 20 = ...
b $\frac{3}{4}$ of 20 = ...

Fractions, percentages, ratio and proportion (calculator allowed)

4 *2004 Progress Test level 4*

a Gold ribbon costs 60p for one metre. Tom has £2.40.
How many metres of gold ribbon can he buy?

b Blue ribbon costs 40p for one metre. Nicola buys $3\frac{1}{2}$ metres.
How much does this cost?

5 *2003 Progress Test level 4*

a Kate is using her computer to print a photo.
The red bar shows how much of the photo is printed so far.

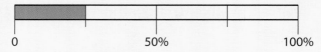

What percentage of the photo is printed so far?

b Each photo takes 20 seconds to print.
How many minutes will it take to print 15 photos?
Show your working.

6 *2004 level 4*

Here are the ingredients for a cordial used to make a drink.

a Jenny is going to make this cordial with 25 g of ginger.
How much lemon, water and sugar should she use?

b The finished drink should be $\frac{1}{3}$ cordial and $\frac{2}{3}$ water.
Jenny puts 100 ml of cordial in a glass.
How much water should she put with it?

> **50 g** ginger
>
> **1** lemon
>
> **1.5** litres water
>
> **900 g** sugar

Probability 2

This unit will help you to:

- describe the chance of an event using words like **certain** or **impossible**;
- describe probabilities using simple fractions;
- know where to place events on a probability scale marked $0, \frac{1}{2}, 1$;
- use probability to make decisions.

1 Probability scale

This lesson will help you to use a probability scale marked $0, \frac{1}{2}$ and 1.

Exercise 1

The probability scale

| impossible | unlikely | even chance | likely | certain |

An event that is **impossible** has a probability of 0.

An event that is **certain** has a probability of 1.

An event that has an **even chance** has a probability of $\frac{1}{2}$.

For example:

- The probability of my teacher going to live on the Moon is 0.
- Today is Wednesday. The probability of tomorrow being Thursday is 1.
- If I flip a coin, the probability of getting a tail is $\frac{1}{2}$.

Other words that describe the likelihood of events include **likely** and **unlikely**.

1 Imagine it is the middle of winter.

Copy and complete the sentences below. Choose from these words:

impossible   certain   likely   unlikely   even chance   very unlikely   almost impossible

You may use a word more than once.

a   It is .... that it will be windy tomorrow.

b   In Scotland it is .... that it will snow somewhere.

c   It is .... that it will be so warm that I won't need to wear a coat today.

d   It is .... that there will be a thunderstorm this week.

e   It is .... that it will be foggy this week.

2 Continue to imagine that it is still the middle of winter.

Copy this probability scale.

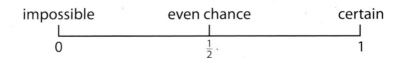

impossible   even chance   certain

0                        $\frac{1}{2}$ 1

Use arrows to mark the probability of A, B and C on the scale.

A   Tomorrow all trees will have leaves on them.

B   The new year will begin this winter.

C   One day this week the temperature will be below zero.

3 The weather can change from day to day.

Copy this probability scale.

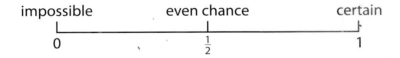

impossible   even chance   certain

0         $\frac{1}{2}$ 1

Use arrows to mark the probability of A, B and C on the scale.

A It is in the middle of summer. Tomorrow there will be snow.

B Tomorrow the sun will rise.

C It is spring time. Tomorrow it will rain.

4 Think about what you've done today so far and what you will do during the rest of the day.

a Give an event in your day that has probability 1.

b Give an event in your day that has probability $\frac{1}{2}$.

c Give an event in your day that has probability 0.

5 These sentences describe the weather in different countries of the world.

Pick a country from the list to match each sentence:

Australia   Ethiopia   Lapland   Italy   Ireland

You may use each country only once.

a In this country the probability that it will snow in the winter is 1.

b In this country the probability that it will snow in the winter is 0.

c In this country the probability that the middle of summer is in January is 1.

d In this country the probability of a rainy day in the spring is $\frac{1}{2}$.

e In this country the probability that the temperature in June will be below freezing is 0.

6 Now imagine it is summer.

Write a sentence about the probability of the weather in the summer using these numbers.

a 1   b $\frac{1}{2}$ c 0

⊙ **Points to remember**

⊙ You can use numbers to describe the likelihood of events:
 – 0 for impossible;
 – 1 for certain;
 – $\frac{1}{2}$ for an even chance.

⊙ A probability scale can show how likely or unlikely events are.

impossible	unlikely	even chance	likely	certain
0		$\frac{1}{2}$		1

2 Probability games

This lesson will help you to use probability to understand some simple games.

> ## ⓘ **Did you know that...?**
>
> Playing dice was very popular among the **Romans**.
>
> This is a picture of a Roman dice.
> The dice were called *tesserae*.
>
> Three dice were shaken in a cup and then thrown.
> People used to try to guess the outcome.
>
> The Romans also used animals' knucklebones as dice.
> These had four sides. They were called *tali*.

A Roman dice

Exercise 2

In a game players take turns to toss a coin.
They move along a track depending on whether they get a head or a tail.

The track below shows a part-completed game.

Issie (heads)										
Paul (tails)										

Paul is in the lead at this point. There have been two more tails tossed than heads.

The game is **fair** because each player has an **equal chance** of winning.

1. Four friends play a game. One player is red, one is yellow, one is blue and one is green.

   They take turns to spin this spinner.

   The player whose colour comes up scores a point.

   The winner is the first to get 5 points.

   Is this a fair game? Explain your answer.

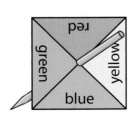

Work with a partner. You need a dice, two counters and **S2.4 Resource sheet 2.1**.

2   Play **Racing car game 1**. Follow the instructions on **Resource sheet 2.1**.

   a   Which car won?

   b   Is this a fair game? Explain your answer.

   c   What number car would you choose next time? Why?

3   Play **Racing car game 2**. Follow the instructions on **Resource sheet 2.1**.

   a   Which car won?

   b   What is the probability that the silver car will win? Explain your answer.

   c   Is this a fair game? Explain your answer.

   d   What colour racing car would you choose next time? Why?

Extension problem

4   a   The silver car and the white car have another race.
       Here are the new rules.
       Silver moves if there is a prime number on the dice.
       White moves if there is not a prime number.

       Is this a fair game? Explain your answer.

   b   Make up your own rule for moving the cars.
       Play the game.
       Do both cars have the same chance of winning?

Points to remember

• In a **fair** game, everyone has an equal chance of winning.

3 Equally likely outcomes

This lesson will help you to find out more about equally likely outcomes and what a 'fair game' is.

Exercise 3

Equally likely outcomes have an equal chance of happening.

A dice has six faces labelled 1 to 6.

Each number has an equal chance of coming up.

The numbers 1, 2, 3, 4, 5 and 6 are equally likely.

The chance of getting an **odd number** with a dice is $\frac{1}{2}$.

The chance of getting an **even number** with a dice is $\frac{1}{2}$.

Work with a partner. You will need a bag, some coloured counters, a matchstick, some coloured pens, scissors and a copy of **S2.4 Resource sheet 3.1** between you.

1 **a** Put six counters, each of a different colour, in the bag.

Take turns to pick a counter and write down its colour.
Put the counter back in the bag.
Do this 20 times altogether.

Is each colour equally likely? Explain your answer.

b Put in the bag three counters of one colour and three more, each of a different colour. For example, red, red, red, blue, yellow, green.

Take turns to pick a counter and write down its colour.
Put the counter back in the bag.
Do this 10 times altogether.

Is each colour equally likely? Explain your answer.

② Do an experiment with a bag and counters.

Player A secretly puts some counters in the bag.
They can be of any colour.
You can put in more than one of some colours if you like.

Player B picks a counter out of the bag.
Write down the colour, then put the counter back.
Do this 20 times.

a How many of each colour does player B think there are?
Explain why.

b Is each colour equally likely? How do you know?

c Player A should now take the counters out of the bag.
Show player B the counters.
Was player B right?

d Now change over. This time player B puts the counters in the bag secretly.
Answer questions a to c again.

③ Colour and cut out the spinners on **S2.4 Resource sheet 3.1**.

Make a small hole in the middle so you can put them on a stick and spin them.

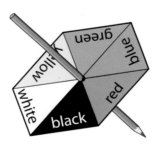

a On some of the spinners each colour is equally likely.
Which spinners?

b Each of you should pick a spinner.
Spin your spinner 20 times, recording your results.

Which spinner did you pick?
Are your results what you expected? Explain what your results show.

Points to remember

⊙ **Equally likely outcomes** have an equal chance of happening.

⊙ In a **fair game** all the players have an equal chance of winning.

How well are you doing?

Can you:

- describe probability and likelihood using words like 'certain' or 'impossible'?
- write probabilities using simple fractions?
- place events on a probability scale marked 0, $\frac{1}{2}$, 1?
- use probability to tell if a game is fair?

1 *KS2 2005 level 4*

Sapna makes up a game using seven cards.
Here are the cards.

1 2 3 4 5 6 7

Josh picks a card without looking.

If Josh picks an odd number, then Sapna scores a point.
If Josh picks an even number, then Josh scores a point.

Is this a fair game? Explain how you know.

2 *KS2 2001 level 4*

Here are two spinners, A and B.
Each one is a regular hexagon.

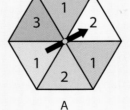 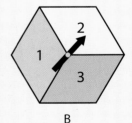

A   B

a For each statement, say whether it is
   True or **False**.

   i   Scoring 1 is more likely on A than on B.

   ii Scoring 2 is more likely on A than on B.

   iii Scoring 3 is as equally likely on A as on B.

b Zara spins both spinners. The score on A is added to the score on B.
   She says: 'The sum of the scores on both spinners is certain to be less than 7.'

   Is she correct? Explain how you know.

KS2 1996 level 4

Here are two spinners.

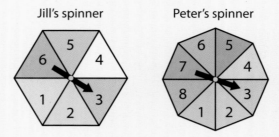

Jill's spinner   Peter's spinner

a Jill says: 'I am more likely than Peter to spin a 3.'
   Give a reason why she is correct.

b Peter says: 'We are both equally likely to spin an even number.'
   Give a reason why he is correct.

Properties of shapes

This unit will help you to:

- recognise parallel and perpendicular lines;
- know and use the sum of angles in a triangle;
- recognise properties of squares and rectangles;
- sort 2D shapes according to their properties;
- draw 2D shapes on grids;
- make 2D and 3D shapes from polygons;
- identify and draw nets of 3D shapes.

1 Parallel and perpendicular lines

This lesson will help you to recognise parallel and perpendicular lines.

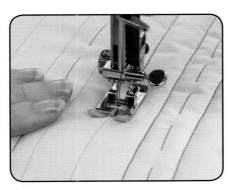

Exercise 1

Parallel lines are straight lines that are always the same distance apart. They never meet.

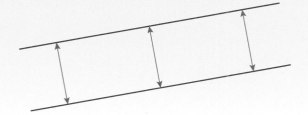

Perpendicular lines are straight lines that cross at right angles (90°).

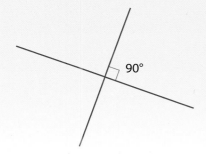

90°

You will need coloured pencils, a sharp pencil, a ruler and a protractor.

1　Look at this picture.

Do the lines look as though they are sets of parallel and perpendicular lines?

Use your ruler to help you to find sets of parallel lines.

2　Look at this pattern.
It was made using a ruler on squared paper.

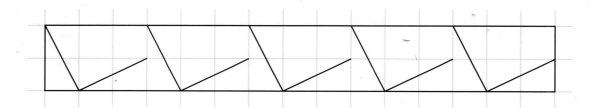

a　Copy the pattern on squared paper.
Mark each set of parallel lines a different colour.
How many different sets of parallel line are there?

b　Make another copy of the pattern on squared paper.
Use colour to show where there are pairs of perpendicular lines.
Describe where these sets of lines are in the diagram.

c　On your squared paper, make up two more patterns of your own.
On each of them mark and colour some sets of parallel lines and perpendicular lines.

3 You need a copy of **G2.5 Resource sheet 1.1**.

a On the resource sheet, colour the parallel lines in this diagram.
Colour each set of parallel lines a different colour.

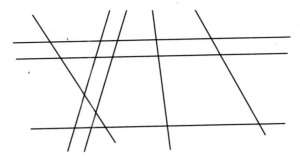

b Use a coloured pencil to show the right angles in each diagram.

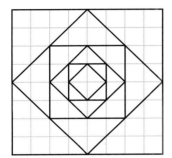 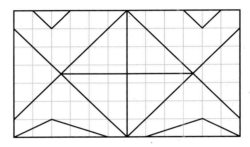

> **Points to remember**
>
> ⊙ **Parallel lines** are always the same distance apart. They never meet.
> ⊙ **Perpendicular lines** cross at right angles.
> ⊙ You can use these properties to identify and describe shapes.

2 Properties of shapes

This lesson will help you to describe the properties of different shapes.

Exercise 2

Triangles are polygons with three sides.

There are four types of triangle: **equilateral**, **isosceles**, **right-angled** and **scalene**.

Quadrilaterals are polygons with four sides.

Some special quadrilaterals are:

square, rectangle, parallelogram, rhombus, kite, arrowhead, trapezium.

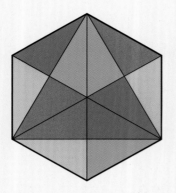

This pattern is made from **right-angled triangles**.

Two of the same colour fit together to make a **kite**.

Four of them, one of each colour, fit together to make a **rhombus**.

What other shapes can you see in the pattern?

Can you see some **isosceles triangles**?

Can you see some **equilateral triangles**?

What shape is the whole pattern?

Example

What is the name of this shape?
Describe its properties.

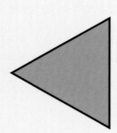

This is an equilateral triangle.
It has three sides of equal length.
The three angles are the same size.
It has three lines of symmetry.

1. Work in a group of four to play **Guess the shape**. You will need a set of cards made from **G2.5 Resource sheet 2.1**.

Rules

◉ Shuffle the cards. Spread them face down on the table.

◉ Take turns to take a card. Keep it secret.

◉ Tell the group about your shape.

   a How many sides does it have?
      Are any of its sides equal in length?

   b How many pairs of parallel sides are there?

   c How many right angles does it have?

   d Are any of its angles equal?

   e How many lines of symmetry does it have?

◉ Ask others in the group to guess the name of your shape.

◉ Carry on until you have used all the cards.

2 Pick one of the shapes from the **Guess the shape** cards.
Write its name, draw it into your book, then answer these questions.

    a How many sides does your shape have?

    b How many of its sides are equal in length?

    c How many pairs of parallel sides does it have?

    d How many right angles does it have?

    e Are any of its angles equal?

    f How many lines of symmetry does it have?

3   **a** Write the names of three shapes with four sides.
      Use the cards from **Guess the shape** to help you.

    b Write the names of three shapes that have at least one right angle.

    c Write the names of three shapes that have at least two sides of equal length.

4 Draw a square and a rectangle.

    a What properties do they both have?

    b In what ways are they different?

Extension problem

   a John said:
      'A quadrilateral can have only three right angles.'
      Is he correct? Explain your answer.

    b Ismat said:
      'A triangle can have two lines of symmetry.'
      Is she correct? Explain your answer.

    c Leroy said:
      'The diagonals of some quadrilaterals cross at right angles.'
      Is he correct? Explain your answer.

Points to remember

⊙ You can describe a shape using properties such as:
    – the number of sides, and whether they are the parallel or
      equal in length;
    – the number of right angles and any equal angles;
    – the number of lines of symmetry.

3 Classifying shapes

This lesson will help you to sort polygons according to their properties.

 Did you know that...?

A shape with seven sides is called a **heptagon**.

A shape with a thousand sides is called a **chiliagon**.

A shape with a million sides is called a **hecatommyriagon**.

Exercise 3

All the sides of a **regular shape** are equal in length and all the angles are the same size.

No. of sides	Name	Example	Regular shape
3	triangle		
4	quadrilateral		
5	pentagon		
6	hexagon		
7	heptagon		
8	octagon		
9	nonagon		
10	decagon		

You will need the shape cards from **G2.5 Resource sheet 2.1** and **G2.5 Resource sheet 3.1** and some scissors. Alternatively, you could use a set of plastic polygons.

For questions 1 to 4, work in a group of four.

1 Cut out the triangles on **G2.5 Resource sheet 3.1**, or use a set of plastic triangles. Use the sorting diagram below to sort them into groups.

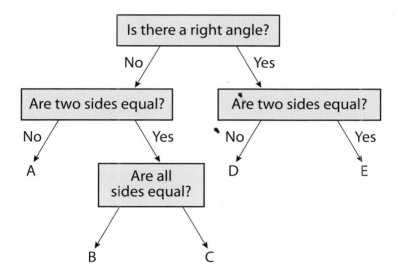

Write the different types of triangles that end at A, B, C, D and E.

2 You will need the cards from **G2.5 Resource sheet 2.1** for this question, or some plastic polygons.

Identify the shapes.

a Which shape has one pair of parallel lines?

b Two shapes have more than four sides.
Name them both.

c Which shape has one line of symmetry and two pairs of equal sides?

d Which shapes have at least one right angle?

e Which shapes are regular shapes?

f Choose two shapes.
For each shape, write its name and describe one of its properties.

③ You will need the cards from **G2.5 Resource sheet 2.1,** or some plastic polygons for this question.

   a   Sort the shapes into two groups.
       Describe how you sorted them.

   b   Sort them again into two groups. The groups should be different from question **a**.
       Describe how you sorted them.

   c   Sort the shapes into three groups.
       Describe how you sorted them.

④ You need some squared paper.

   a   On squared paper, draw a triangle with no right angles.

   b   Now draw a quadrilateral with no right angles.

⊙ Points to remember

⊙ You can identify and sort shapes according to properties such as:
   – number of sides;
   – number of sides of equal length;
   – number of pairs of parallel sides;
   – number of right angles;
   – number of equal angles;
   – number of lines of symmetry.

---

4 Angles

This lesson will help you to calculate angles in a triangle.

Exercise 4

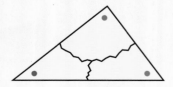

The angles in a triangle add up to 180°.

This means that if you know two of the angles in a triangle you can work out the third.

This is called **calculating the angles in a triangle**.

If you are asked to calculate the angles, you must not use a protractor to measure them.

Example

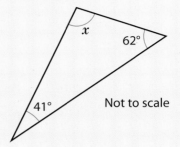

Calculate the size of angle x.

One angle is 41°.

Another angle is 62°.

These two angles add up to 62° + 41° = 103°.

The third angle is 180 − 103° = 77°, because the three angles of a triangle add up to 180°.

Not to scale

---

1 Look at this quadrilateral.

a Which angle is a right angle?

b Which angle is an acute angle?

c Name one angle that is an obtuse angle.

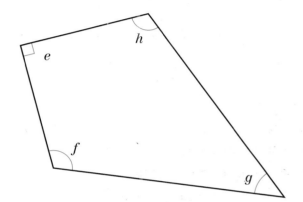

2 Two of these angles are the same size.

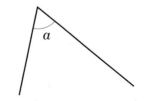 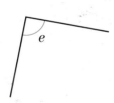

Which two angles are they?

3 Look at these angles.

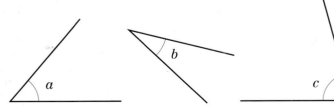  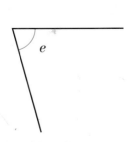

a Which angle is about 25°?

b Which angle is about 125°?

4 These triangles are all right-angled.
Calculate the missing angles. Show your working.

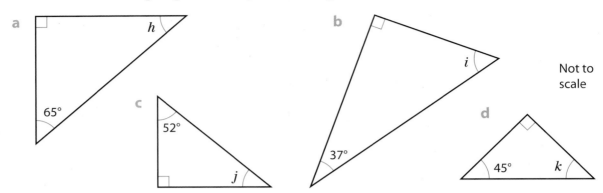

a

b

c

d

Not to scale

5 The diagram shows a square.

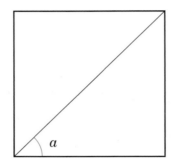

How many degrees is angle *a*? Explain how you know.

6 Calculate the missing angle in each of these triangles. Show your working.

a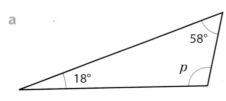

b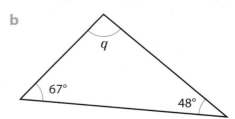

c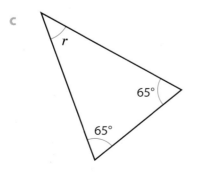

d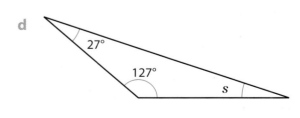

7 These triangles are all isosceles.
Calculate the missing angles. Show your working.

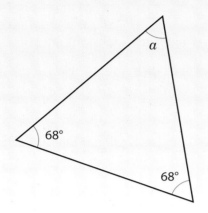

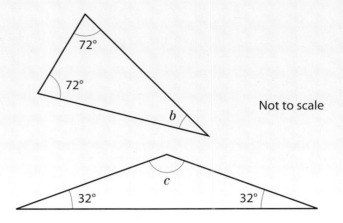

Not to scale

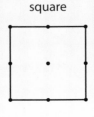

⊙ **Points to remember**

⊙ The **three angles of a triangle** always add up to **180°**.

⊙ If you know two of the angles in a triangle, you can **calculate** the third.

⊙ Calculate means to work out without measuring.

---

5 Drawing 2D shapes on grids

This lesson will help you to draw 2D shapes on grids.

Exercise 5

These shapes are drawn on dotty paper.

The dots can help you to work out which sides are equal and which angles are right angles.

triangle   rectangle   square   pentagon

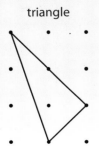

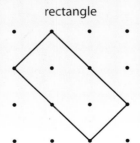

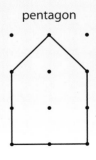

You will need some square dotty paper, a pencil and a ruler.

1. Take turns to **Make a square** with a partner.

   Rules

   - Player 1: Pick two spots on the dotty paper and join them with a straight line.
   - Player 2: Complete a drawing of a square using the line as one side.
   - Player 1: Check that the drawing is a square.
     If it isn't, complete the square yourself.

   The first few times, choose two dots close together. Don't make it too hard!

   Then try using pairs of dots that make the line at an angle.

   How can you be sure that you have drawn a square each time?

2. Use the dots to draw:

   a. a quadrilateral that has no right angles

   b. a quadrilateral with exactly one right angle

   c. a quadrilateral with exactly two right angles

   d. a pentagon with exactly three right angles.

3. a. Draw some rectangles that are twice as long as they are wide. Write down their sizes.

   b. Draw some rectangles that have a line like the one on the right as one of the sides.

   c. Draw a rectangle with the line shown as one side AND where the rectangle is twice as long as it is wide.

   d. Find another rectangle with the line shown as one side AND where the rectangle is twice as long as it is wide.

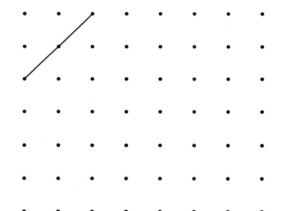

> ◉ **Points to remember**
>
> ⊙ Use the properties of polygons to:
>   - help you to identify them;
>   - help you to draw them on a grid.

6 Making shapes and solids

This lesson will help you to make shapes and solids by matching faces and edges.

 ## Did you know that...?

A **tangram** is a very old Chinese puzzle. The pieces fit together to make a square.

This tangram has seven pieces.

It is said that a servant of a Chinese emperor was carrying an expensive and fragile tile. The servant tripped and broke the tile.

The servant could not put the pieces back into a square.

Instead he made pictures from them.

You will need a copy of **G2.5 Resource sheet 6.1** and some scissors.

Hint: Sometimes you need to turn the parallelogram over.

1. Cut out the shapes on G2.5 Resource sheet 6.1.

    a   Write down the names of the three different shapes.

    b   Put the pieces in order of size, from smallest to largest.

    c   Can you find any connections between the sizes of the pieces?

    d   Find the two identical right-angled triangles.
        Draw all the different shapes you can make with the two pieces.

2. Use the tangram pieces to make these squares.
    Sketch your answers in your book.

    a   Make a square with one tangram piece.

    b   Make a square with two tangram pieces.

    c   Make a square with three tangram pieces.

    d   Make a square with four tangram pieces.

    e   Make a square with five tangram pieces.

3. Use all seven of the tangram pieces to make these shapes.
    Sketch your answers in your book.

    a   parallelogram   b   right-angled triangle

    c   hexagon   d   rectangle

4. Just for fun, try making these pictures, or make up some of your own.
    If you wish, you could try making some numbers or letters.

Points to remember

⊙ Solid shapes have edges, faces and vertices.

⊙ You can make new shapes by matching:
- sides of 2D shapes;
- faces of identical cubes.

7 Nets

This lesson will help you to know the nets of simple 3D shapes.

Did you know that...?

3D shapes are called **solids**.
The faces of these solids are identical regular polygons:

 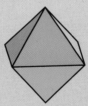 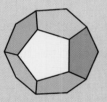 

| tetrahedron | cube | octahedron | dodecahedron | icosahedron |

The **tetrahedron** is a special pyramid. It has 4 faces that are equilateral triangles.

The **cube** has 6 square faces.

The **octahedron** has 8 equilateral triangular faces.

The **dodecahedron** has 12 pentagonal faces.

The **icosahedron** has 20 equilateral triangular faces.

These five solids are named by the ancient Greek mathematician **Plato.**

Exercise 7

A **net** is the flat shape that folds up to make a 3D shape.

For example, this is the net of a cube.

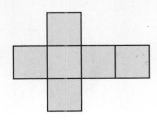

You will need a ruler, scissors, squared paper and a sharp pencil.

① The diagram shows all the different shapes that can be made with five identical squares. These are called **pentominoes.**

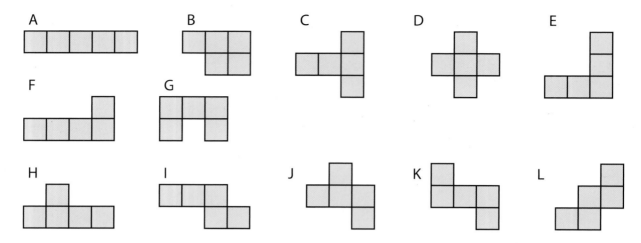

a   Look at each one very carefully.
   Which of them are the nets of an open box (a cube with no lid)?

b   Copy onto squared paper the ones you think are nets of an open box.
   Cut the nets out.
   Fold them up to check that they make an open box.

② This diagram shows part of a net of a cube.

a   Make four copies of the diagram on squared paper.
   Mark on each of them a different way of adding a square to make a net of a cube.

b   Cut out your nets and check your answers.

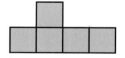

③ This diagram shows a cuboid 2 cm long, 1 cm high and 1 cm wide.

On centimetre squared paper, draw an accurate net for this cuboid.
Cut it out and fold it up to check.

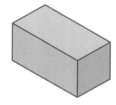

> ◉ **Points to remember**
> ⊙ A **net** is the flat shape that folds up to make a 3D shape.
> ⊙ When you draw a net, arrange the faces so that they match up when the net is cut out and folded up.

How well are you doing?

Can you:

- sort polygons according to their properties?
- calculate a missing angle in a triangle?
- draw 2D shapes on grids?
- make 2D and 3D shapes from polygons?
- identify and draw nets of 3D shapes?

You will need squared paper for question 4.

1 *2005 Progress Test level 4*

Here is a net of a 3D shape.

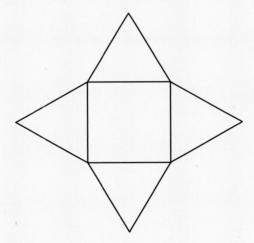

When the net is folded, what 3D shape will it make?

Choose the correct answer from this list:

cube   prism   square-based pyramid   triangular-based pyramid   cuboid

2 *2006 Progress Test level 4*

Look at the shaded shape on the square grid.

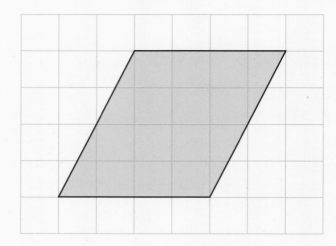

For each statement below, say if it is **True** or **False**.

a The shaded shape is a quadrilateral.

b The shaded shape has four equal sides.

c The shaded shape has four equal angles.

d The shaded shape has two pairs of parallel sides.

3 *2003 Progress Test level 4*

Look at this shape.

Copy and complete the sentences:

a The shape is a square so the sides must be …………

b The shape is a square so the angles must be …………

4 *1995 KS2 level 4*

You will need some squared paper.

On the paper draw a quadrilateral.

It must have only one pair of parallel sides.

Functional skills 3

Making jeans

This group activity will help you to:

- work out how to tackle an unfamiliar problem;
- choose and use the mathematics needed to solve it;
- explain and justify your solution.

Background

When companies make clothes they have to think about a number of things so that they make a profit.

Here are some of the factors that have to be considered

- Who is likely to buy them? What will they pay?
- What does the material cost?
- What are the labour costs?
- How many pairs of jeans are they likely to sell?
- How much profit can the company make?

Background information

It takes 1.25 metres of denim to make a pair of jeans.

Denim costs £3.60 a metre.

You can only buy a whole number of metres of the denim.

Manufacturers generally aim to make a profit of 50% on jeans.

The profit is how much money you make after you have paid for the cost of making the jeans.

Problems

1 The material

a How much does the material for one pair of jeans cost?

b How much extra will you pay for the unused denim?

c How many pairs of jeans will you need to make if you don't want to waste any denim?

2 Pricing

Labour and trimmings like zips add 50% to the cost of the denim for making one pair of jeans.
Altogether, how much does one pair of jeans cost to make?

3 Profits

a What will the price of the jeans need to be in order to make a 10% profit?

b How many pairs of jeans will you need to sell to make a 10% profit of at least £100?

c What if you wanted to make a 50% profit of at least £100?
How many pairs of jeans will you need to sell?

Discuss in pairs and ask other questions about making jeans.

Expressions and equations

This unit will help you to:

- ◎ do number operations in the right order, and use brackets;
- ◎ use letters for numbers;
- ◎ simplify an expression;
- ◎ use inverse operations to solve simple equations.

1 Order of operations

This lesson will help you to do number operations in the right order.

Exercise 1

These two calculators work in different ways.

Scientific calculator

Basic calculator

If you do 3 + 5 × 2 on the scientific calculator you get 13.

It does 5 × 2 first, then + 3.

If you do 3 + 5 × 2 on the basic calculator you get 16.

It does 3 + 5 first, then × 2.

The basic calculator works things out in the order you enter them. The scientific calculator works things out in the correct order.

Always do multiplication and division before addition and subtraction.

1. Copy these. Replace each box by = or ≠.

   a 9 + 16 ☐ 16 + 9

   b 23 − 14 ☐ 14 − 23

   c 8 × 17 ☐ 17 × 8

   d 27 + 39 ☐ 29 + 27

   e 45 ÷ 9 ☐ 9 ÷ 45

   f 72 − 34 ☐ 34 − 72

2. **True** or **False**? If **False**, write the correct answer.

   a 5 × 4 + 8 = 28

   b 10 × 3 − 19 = 8

   c 16 + 7 × 2 = 30

   d 30 − 9 × 3 = 63

   e 36 ÷ 6 + 4 = 10

   f 24 ÷ 6 − 4 = 12

   g 12 + 9 ÷ 3 = 7

   h 33 − 28 ÷ 7 = 29

3. Work out the answers.

   a 6 × 2 + 9

   b 5 × 7 − 24

   c 15 + 7 × 2

   d 100 − 10 × 2

   e 24 ÷ 3 + 5

   f 50 ÷ 5 − 3

   g 14 + 6 ÷ 2

   h 25 − 40 ÷ 4

4. Write the calculation needed to solve the problem.
   Then work out the answer.

   a Gran gave Ben a £10 note.
      Mum gave him four £5 notes.
      How much did Ben get altogether?

   b Sami gave a shopkeeper a 50p coin.
      She gave him three 10p coins as change.
      How much did Sami pay altogether?

   c Katie wanted a game console.
      She paid a £25 deposit..
      She then paid 12 monthly payments of £7.
      How much did Katie pay altogether?

   d Denzie had a bag of 35 sweets.
      She gave three sweets each to seven of her friends.
      How many sweets did Denzie have left?

5 Write a problem for each of these.

   a $3 \times 4 + 8$ b $7 \times 6 - 3$ c $1 + 5 \times 2$

   d $14 - 2 \times 3$ e $10 + 4 \times 2$ f $30 + 5 \times 7$

Extension problem

6 Write the calculation needed to solve the problem.
Then work out the answer.

   a A driver had driven 9000 miles in his car.
       He then drove 42 miles each day for five days.
       How many miles did he drive altogether?

   b Iram had £150 in her savings account.
       She then put in £5 a month for 15 months.
       What is the total in her account after 15 months?

 Points to remember

- You can change the order of the numbers when you add or multiply, so:
  $5 + 3 = 3 + 5$
  $4 \times 2 = 2 \times 4$
- You can't change the order when you subtract or divide, so:
  $5 - 3 \neq 3 - 5$
  $4 \div 2 \neq 2 \div 4$
- Multiply and divide before you add and subtract.

2 Using brackets

This lesson will help you to use brackets.

Exercise 2

If there are no brackets, do multiplication and division before addition and subtraction.
   $4 + 3 \times 7 = 4 + 21 = 25$

You can change the order of operations by adding brackets.
Do what is inside the brackets first.
   $(4 + 3) \times 7 = 7 \times 7 = 49$

1. Jessica did these questions in a test.

   Look at each question.
   Did she get it right or wrong?

   a $4 \times (1 + 5) = 24$

   b $(22 - 17) \times 10 = 50$

   c $7 + 3 \times 5 = 50$

   d $54 - 9 \times 6 = 0$

   e $(41 + 7) \div 8 = 6$

   f $45 - 35 \div 5 = 2$

   g $11 + 3 \times 7 = 98$

   h $8 \times (26 - 21) = 40$

2. Copy these equations.
   Put brackets where they are needed to make the calculations correct.

   a $6 + 2 \times 6 = 48$

   b $7 - 3 \times 9 = 36$

   c $15 + 8 \times 4 = 47$

   d $18 - 4 \times 3 = 6$

   e $8 + 24 \div 4 = 8$

   f $33 - 6 \div 3 = 9$

   g $4 \times 8 + 2 = 40$

   h $56 \div 3 + 5 = 7$

3. You need **A2.3 Resource sheet 2.1**.

   Complete the cross-number puzzle on
   the resource sheet.

4. You can use the digits 2, 3 and 4, with $+$, $-$, $\times$ or $\div$, or brackets, to make the number 2.

   $$(2 + 4) \div 3 = 2$$

   Use the digits 2, 3 and 4, with any of $+$, $-$, $\times$ or $\div$, or brackets, to make these.

   a 11   b 4   c 18   d 10

   e 5   f 14   g 20   h 1

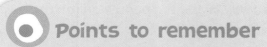

Points to remember

- If there are brackets, do what is inside the brackets first.
- If there are no brackets, multiply and divide before you add and subtract.

3 Letters for numbers

This lesson will help you to use letters to represent numbers.

 Did you know that...?

Mohammed Al-Khwarizmi developed the algebra that we do today. His picture is on the stamp.

Mohammed was born around 780.
He died when he was about 70 years old.
He worked at the House of Wisdom for the Caliph who ruled Baghdad.

He wrote a book called *Hisab al-jabr w'al-muqabala*. The word 'algebra' comes from its title.

Exercise 3

You can use a letter to represent any number.

Example 1

Femi is thinking of a number n. He adds 12 and gets 26. What is the number n?

$n + 12 = 26$, so n must be 14.

Example 2

James picks a apples from a tree.
Kate picks 4 more apples than James.
Write an expression for the number of apples that Kate picks.

Kate picks the same number of apples as James, plus 4 more.
She picks $a + 4$ apples.

1 **a** There are n people on a bus. Five more people get on the bus.
How many people are now on the bus?

b There are n people on a bus. Two people get off the bus.
How many people are now on the bus?

c There are six buses. Each bus has n passengers.
What is the total number of passengers?

2 I think of a number n. Write an expression for the number I get when I:

a add 5 to n

b subtract 3 from n

c multiply n by 3

d divide n by 6

e add n to 7

f subtract n from 10

3 Caitlin eats q pieces of chocolate.

Write a sentence to describe:

a $q + 7$

b $q - 4$

c $2q$

d $q \div 3$

4 Tom is x years old.
Write expressions for these.

$x - 3$

a Zeenat is 3 years younger than Tom.
How old is Zeenat?

b Jafar is four times as old as Tom.
How old is Jafar?

c Alice is 8 years older than Tom.
How old is Alice?

d Chris is half as old as Tom.
How old is Chris?

5 Tina is m centimetres tall. Write expressions for these.

   a Henry is twice as tall as Tina. How tall is Henry?

   b Jack is 10 cm taller than Tina. How tall is Jack?

   c Petra is 6 cm shorter than Tina. How tall is Petra?

6 Work out the number n.

   a I add 3 to n. I get 57.   **b** I subtract 18 from n. I get 10.

   c I multiply n by 2. I get 40.   **d** I divide n by 6. I get 7.

   e I add 40 to n. I get 120.   **f** I subtract 53 from n. I get 40.

◉ Points to remember

- ⊙ Letters can represent numbers.
- ⊙ The expression $n + 5$ tells you to 'add the number 5 to the number n'.
- ⊙ $6b$ means $6 \times b$.

---

4 Collecting like terms

This lesson will help you to simplify an expression.

Exercise 4

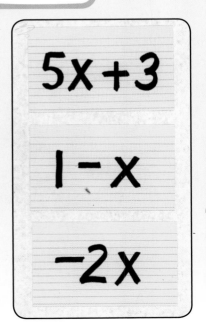

A **term** is a number or letter, or numbers or letters that are multiplied together. In the expression

$$3 + 4a + 5ab$$

3, $4a$, and $5ab$ are all terms.

Like terms have the same letters in them. For example:

   a, $3a$ and $7a$ are all like terms;

   $4a$ and $3b$ are not like terms.

You can add and subtract like terms.

Example

Write as simply as you can $4a + 7a + b$.

$$4a + 7a + b = 11a + b$$

1. Copy these. Underline each term.

   a $9 + b$

   b $a + 2c$

   c $3d - 4$

   d $ab + cd$

   e $p + qr$

   f $6mn + 5$

2. Copy these. Underline like terms using the same colour.

   a $4 + 2a + 9$

   b $4b + 2c - 3b$

   c $p + 5p - 6q$

   d $8 + 2s - 3 + 4s$

   e $q + 7r + 4q - 3$

   f $9x + 2y - 5x - 4y$

3. Write these as simply as you can.

   a $2p + 6p$

   b $3b + 7b$

   c $x + 3x$

   d $7y - y$

   e $7a - 5a$

   f $9b - 4b$

   g $2n - n$

   h $m + m$

4. Which two of these cannot be simplified?

   $$x + x + y \qquad 2x + y \qquad x + 2y \qquad x + y + y$$

5. Write these as simply as you can.

   a $6 + 4a + 7a$

   b $4x + 7x + 8$

   c $2y + 7y - 3y + 2z$

   d $3a + 8a - a + 4b + 2b$

   e $7a + 9b + 6a + 4b$

   f $10m + 3n + 7m - n$

6. Charles has n marbles.
   Write expressions for these.

   a James has twice as many marbles as Charles.
      How many marbles does James have?

   b Jake has four times as many marbles as Charles.
      How many marbles does Jake have?

   c How many marbles do the three boys have altogether?

7. Which two of these cannot be simplified?

   $$2a + 3a - 4 \qquad 3x + 4y - 2x \qquad 4x - 3 + 2y \qquad 2x + 4y + 3$$

Extension problem

8 Tea costs x pence per cup.
Coffee costs y pence per mug.

Mandy buys 4 mugs of coffee and 3 cups of tea.
She then buys 3 mugs of coffee and 2 cups of tea.
How much does Mandy pay altogether?

Write your answer as simply as you can.

Points to remember

- **Like terms** have the same combination of letters.
  For example, a, $3a$ and $7a$ are like terms.
- You can **simplify** an expression by combining like terms.
  For example, $3a + 7a = 10a$

5 Substitution

This lesson will help you to substitute numbers for letters in an expression.

Exercise 5

You can substitute a number for a letter.

Example

The formula shows how to work out the perimeter of a square.

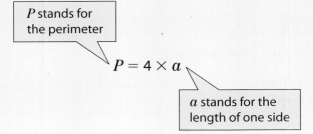

P stands for the perimeter

$P = 4 \times a$

a stands for the length of one side

Leena draws a square with side 7 cm. How long is the perimeter?

Substitute the value 7 for a in $P = 4 \times a$.

So $P = 4 \times 7 = 28$ cm.

1. Work out the value of $x + 9$ when:

   a $x = 5$ b $x = 2$ c $x = 10$

   d $x = 4$ e $x = 25$ f $x = 120$

2. Work out the value of $y - 8$ when:

   a $y = 10$ b $y = 26$ c $y = 15$

   d $y = 34$ e $y = 53$ f $y = 72$

3. Work out the value of $7b$ when:

   a $b = 4$ b $b = 6$ c $b = 2$

   d $b = 10$ e $b = 9$ f $b = 7$

4. Work out the value of $c \div 4$ when:

   a $c = 20$ b $c = 4$ c $c = 36$

   d $c = 24$ e $c = 16$ f $c = 48$

5. Play **Make the most** with a partner.
   You need a dice.

   Rules

   ◉ Take turns to pick one of these cards.
      Choose a different card each time.

$n + 6$	$5n$	$n - 1$	$n \div 2$	$2n + 1$
$2n - 1$	$4n - 3$	$n + 8$	$10n$	$3n - 2$

   ◉ Each of you rolls the dice.
      If the second player rolls the same number as the first, the second player rolls again.

   ◉ Each player substitutes their score for n in the expression on the card.

   ◉ The player who makes the biggest number gets 1 point.

   ◉ The winner is the first player to get 8 points.

6 Work out the value of each of these when $c = 2$.

a 2c

b $c + 4$

c $c - 1$

d $2c + 3$

e $4c - 1$

f $2c - 2$

7 The price of a one-day travel card for the London Underground is £5.

Wendy buys n travel cards for a group of people.
She works out the total cost C like this.

$$C = 5n$$

Work out the total cost for groups of:

a 5 people

b 8 people

c 2 people

d 20 people

Extension problem

8 Eric makes a pattern with hexagonal tiles.
For every n blue tiles he needs $4n + 2$ red tiles.

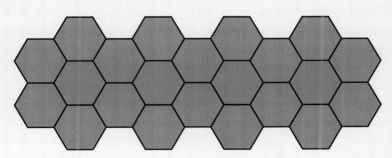

Work out how many red tiles he needs for these values of n.

a $n = 6$

b $n = 12$

c $n = 15$

d $n = 22$

Points to remember

- $2n + 1$ is an **expression**.
  n stands for any number.
- You can **substitute** a number for a letter.
  When $n = 5$, $2n + 1 = 2 \times 5 + 1 = 11$.
- A **formula** shows a relationship.
  The formula for the cost C of n books at £4 each is $C = 4 \times n$.

6 Inverse operations

This lesson will help you to use inverse operations.

Exercise 6

To 'undo' an operation, use its inverse.

- To undo **addition** you do **subtraction**.
- To undo **subtraction** you do **addition**.
- To undo **multiplication** you do **division**.
- To undo **division** you do **multiplication**.

1) Find the output when the input is 9.

   a input → | add 11 | → output

   b input → | subtract 4 | → output

   c input → | divide by 3 | → output

   d input → | multiply by 7 | → output

2) Find the inputs for these function machines.

   a input → | add 15 | → 33

   b input → | subtract 9 | → 14

   c input → | divide by 5 | → 8

   d input → | multiply by 7 | → 56

③ Find the inputs for these function machines.

a input → | add 67 | → 131

b input → | subtract 14 | → 36

c input → | multiply by 11 | → 88

d input → | divide by 5 | → 4

e input → | subtract 59 | → 78

f input → | divide by 3 | → output

g input → | multiply by 3 | → 45

h input → | add 43 | → 150

i input → | divide by 4 | → 7

j input → | add 29 | → 81

k input → | multiply by 10 | → 90

l input → | subtract 27 | → 38

④ At 1 o'clock there were lots of children in the playground.
82 children went indoors.
65 children were left in the playground.

How many children were in the playground at 1 o'clock?

⑤ Some pupils visited the Science Museum.

They went in four groups of 13 pupils.

How many pupils went on the visit?

⑥ Jade played a word game.
She made a word that trebled her score.

This gave her 42 points altogether.

What was Jade's original score?

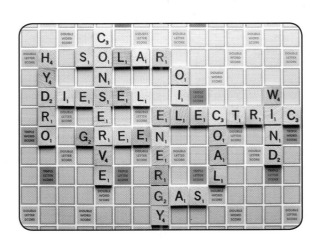

7 Three friends play 'Think of a number' while they are walking home from school.

    a Rachel thinks of a number. She says:

      'Add 3 to my number, then
multiply the result by 5.
The answer is 35.'

      What is Rachel's number?

    b Joe thinks of a number. He says:

      'Add 18 to my number, then
divide the result by 3.
The answer is 30.'

      What is Joe's number?

    c Amy thinks of a number. She says:

      'Halve my number, then add 17.
The answer is 23.'

      What is Amy's number?

Points to remember

- The inverse of $+$ is $-$ and the inverse of $-$ is $+$.
- The inverse of $\times$ is $\div$ and the inverse of $\div$ is $\times$.

7 Solving simple equations

This lesson will help you to use inverse operations to solve simple equations.

Did you know that...?

The ancient Greeks studied patterns that we might think of as functions.

Johann Bernoulli (1667–1748) lived in Switzerland. He was one of the first to study functions in depth.

You can use inverse operations to solve simple equations.

Example 1

Solve $a + 7 = 15$

$$a + 7 = 15 \qquad a \rightarrow \boxed{+7} \rightarrow 15$$

Subtract 7 $\qquad a = 8 \qquad 8 \leftarrow \boxed{-7} \leftarrow 15$

Example 2

Solve $6c = 42$

$$6c = 42 \qquad c \rightarrow \boxed{\times 6} \rightarrow 42$$

Divide by 6 $\qquad c = 7 \qquad 7 \leftarrow \boxed{\div 6} \leftarrow 42$

---

1 Solve these equations.

   a $a + 8 = 19$ b $p + 5 = 21$ c $x + 9 = 35$

   d $b + 4 = 25$ e $d + 10 = 23$ f $y + 7 = 17$

2 Solve these equations.

   a $b - 7 = 3$ b $a - 14 = 6$ c $p - 9 = 8$

   d $q - 8 = 10$ e $m - 10 = 9$ f $x - 6 = 15$

3 Solve these equations.

   a $5x = 45$ b $8p = 48$ c $4c = 28$

   d $3a = 15$ e $9m = 27$ f $6n = 48$

4 Play **Equation Bingo** with a partner.

   Each of you should draw a grid like this.

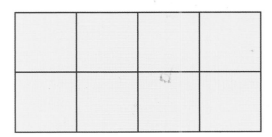

   Each choose eight different numbers from 1 to 15.
   Write the numbers in the spaces on your grid.

Rules

- Take turns to choose one of these equations.
  Choose a different card each time.

$n + 8 = 17$	$c - 8 = 5$	$w \div 2 = 7$	$4 + z = 12$	$h + 9 = 15$
$11 \times f = 22$	$g \div 2 = 2$	$x + 10 = 17$	$16 \div q = 2$	$8 + y = 9$
$m - 9 = 3$	$6 \times p = 30$	$21 - t = 15$	$b - 7 = 4$	$d \div 3 = 5$

- Solve the equation together.
- If either player has the answer on their grid, they cross it out.
- The winner is the first to cross out all their numbers.

5 Copy and complete this table.

a	9	10	7		15
b	6	·		2	
$a + b$		13			
$2a$				16	
$3a$			12		
$a - b$					7

Extension problems

Example 3

Solve $\dfrac{d}{4} = 5$

$$\dfrac{d}{4} = 5 \qquad\qquad d \rightarrow \boxed{\div 4} \rightarrow 5$$

Multiply by 4 $\qquad d = 20 \qquad\qquad 20 \leftarrow \boxed{\times 4} \leftarrow 5$

6 Find the missing number. You may **use your calculator**.

$$32.45 \times \square = 253.11$$

7 Solve these equations.

a $\dfrac{d}{6} = 3$ b $\dfrac{a}{7} = 5$ c $\dfrac{m}{8} = 4$ d $\dfrac{b}{9} = 3$

Points to remember

- You can use inverse operations to solve equations.
- The inverse of $+$ is $-$ and the inverse of $-$ is $+$.
- The inverse of $\times$ is $\div$ and the inverse of $\div$ is $\times$.

How well are you doing?

can you:

- do number operations in the right order?
- use brackets?
- use letters for numbers?
- simplify an expression?
- use inverse operations to solve simple equations?

1 *2002 level 3*

A pupil wrote these calculations. Copy them
Tick (✓) ones that are correct and cross (✗) ones that are wrong.

$4 + 2 = 2 + 4$ $4 - 2 = 2 - 4$

$4 \times 2 = 2 \times 4$ $4 \div 2 = 2 \div 4$

2 *2001 level 4*

Write the answers.

  a $(4 + 2) \times 3$ **b** $4 + 2 \times 3$ **c** $(2 + 4) \times (6 + 3 + 1)$

Put brackets in these calculations to make them correct.

  d $4 + 5 + 1 \times 5 = 50$ **e** $4 + 5 + 1 \times 5 = 34$

3 *2003 Progress Test level 3*

Copy these calculations. Replace each box with a number to make them correct.

  a $36 + \square = 100$ **b** $100 - \square = 51$

  c $\square \times 5 = 100$ **d** $100 \div \square = 25$

4 *2003 Progress Test level 4*

Solve this equation to find the value of m.

  $m - 2 = 8$

2007 Progress Test level 4

Look at this equation.

$$4 + a = b$$

a Write a pair of numbers for a and b to make the equation true.

b Now write a different pair of numbers for a and b to make the equation true.

2006 Progress Test level 4

The equation shows how much you pay to hire a car.

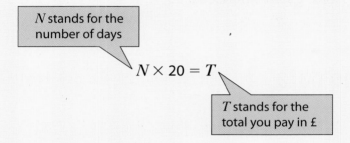

N stands for the number of days

$$N \times 20 = T$$

T stands for the total you pay in £

a Leena hires the car for 10 days.
   How much must she pay?

b Later, Tom pays £280 to hire the car.
   For how many days does he hire the car?

Enquiry 2

This unit will help you to:

- solve a problem by:
  - collecting and organising data;
  - making and interpreting tables, bar charts and line graphs;
  - interpreting pie charts;
- draw simple conclusions;
- write a short report.

1 Collecting data

This lesson will help you to collect and organise data.

Exercise 1

A **tally chart** is a way of recording data as events happen.

Each set of marks stands for a count of five.

These are counted up at the end of the data collection to find the **frequencies**.

Example

Brian is making a list of his baby brother's toy animals.
He records their size and type.

big elephant, small lion, big tiger, medium giraffe, small turtle, small elephant,
medium lion, small elephant, big giraffe, small lion, small turtle, small turtle

Draw a tally chart for the size of animal.

The tally chart shows the number of each size of animal.

Size	Tally	Frequency
Small	III	3
Medium	II	2
Large	IIII II	7

These pictures show lots of different forms of transport. Use them to answer the questions.

1 a Which vehicle in the pictures has the most wheels?

   b Which vehicle has fewest wheels?

2 a Draw a tally chart for the number of wheels in each picture.
     You will need categories for 1, 2, 3, 4 and 5 wheels.

   b Fill in your tally chart and work out the frequencies.

3 Make a tally chart for the type of vehicle.
   You will need categories for cars, bicycles, motorbikes, scooters, tricycles and go-karts.

Points to remember

⊙ When you do a survey, make use of the **data handling cycle**.

⊙ You can use a **tally chart** to collect data.

⊙ Each set of **tally marks** represents a count of five.

⊙ The **frequency** is the total number in a category.

2 Representing data

This lesson will help you to organise data in a table and to draw bar charts.

Exercise 2

This is the data handling cycle.

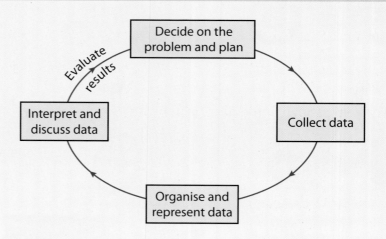

Step 1 Start with the problem. Plan what data to collect to help you to solve it.

Step 2 Then collect the data.

Step 3 Organise and represent your data in tables, charts and graphs.

Step 4 Discuss what the graphs and charts tell you.

Step 5 Decide whether you have now solved the problem.

Example

This **bar chart** shows the number of cycle trips a cycling club made each month.

On the vertical axis, the lines are labelled, not the spaces.

The bars are all the same width and there are gaps between them.

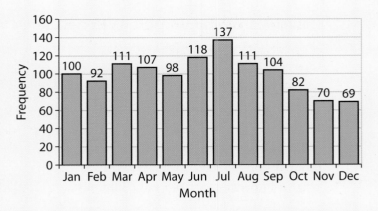

Data source: www.dft.gov.uk

In which month were the most cycle trips made? July

Why do you think this is? It is the summer and the weather is good.

Which months are least popular for cycle trips? November and December

Why do you think this is? The weather is bad and it is dark in the mornings and evenings.

You need either **S2.5 Resource sheet 1.1** from the previous lesson or **S2.5 Resource sheet 2.1**. You will also need squared paper, a ruler and a sharp pencil.

In questions 1–3, start by working out how wide to make the bars of your bar chart and what scale to use on the vertical axis.

1. Draw a bar chart to show your data on the types of vehicles.

2. Draw a bar chart to show your data on the colours of cars.

3. Draw a bar chart to show your data on the numbers of wheels.

Extension problems

4. This table shows some data on vehicles using a country road in 1 hour.

Vehicle type	Tally	Frequency
Motorbikes	III	3
Buses/coaches	I	1
Cars	IIII IIII IIII IIII IIII IIII II	32
Emergency vehicles		0
Lorries	III	3
Vans	IIII IIII I	11

Draw a bar chart to show the data.

5 This table shows some data on vehicles using a main road in 10 minutes.

Vehicle type	Tally	Frequency
Motorbikes	卌	5
Buses/coaches	卌	5
Cars	卌 卌 卌 卌	20
Emergency vehicles	III	3
Lorries	卌 II	7
Vans	卌 卌	10

Draw a bar chart to show the data.

Points to remember

⊙ A **bar chart** is a way of displaying data.

⊙ The height of a bar shows the frequency (total number) for that group.

3 Interpreting data

This lesson will help you to interpret tables, graphs and charts.

Did you know that...?

William Playfair was an engineer and inventor who lived in Dundee in Scotland.

Dundee

One of William Playfair's pie charts

William drew the first ever bar chart in 1786.
He drew the first ever pie chart in 1801.

He said the charts showed data much better than tables did. Do you agree?

Graphs and charts make it easier to see features of a set of data.

For example, it is easy to see the biggest group and the smallest group.
You can also see general trends and patterns.

The most frequent or most popular group is called the **mode**.
This is the highest bar in a bar chart, and the biggest slice in a pie chart.

Example

1200 people were asked which type of
transport is the least safe.

This pie chart shows the results.

What fraction of the people thought that
motorbikes are the least safe ?

About $\frac{3}{4}$ of the people.

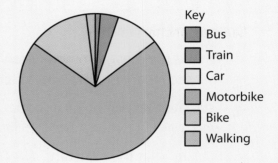

Key
- Bus
- Train
- Car
- Motorbike
- Bike
- Walking

You will need your answers to the questions in Exercise 2.
If you didn't do this work, your teacher will give you **S2.5 Resource sheet 3.1** to
use instead.

1   Look at the bar chart that you drew using the data on types of vehicle.

   a   What was the mode for the type of vehicle?
       Give a possible reason why.

   b   What was the least common type of vehicle?
       Give a possible reason why.

   c   Write a sentence to say what the bar chart tells you.

2   Look at the bar chart you drew to show the data on colours of cars.
    Write two sentences to say what the bar chart tells you.

3   Look at the bar chart that shows the data on numbers of wheels.
    Write two sentences to say what the bar chart tells you.

    Compare your sentences with what you wrote in question 1.
    Is this what you would expect?

4 Look at the pie chart.

   a What is the most common distance that primary pupils travel to school?

   b Estimate the fraction of primary children who travel between 1 and 2 miles.

   c Explain what the pie chart tells you.

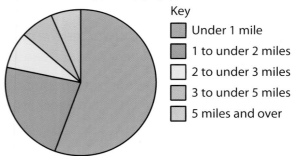

Distances that primary pupils travel to school

Key
- Under 1 mile
- 1 to under 2 miles
- 2 to under 3 miles
- 3 to under 5 miles
- 5 miles and over

Source: www.dft.gov.uk 1999 – 2001

5 Look at the pie chart.

   a What is the most common distance that secondary pupils travel to school?

   b Estimate the fraction of secondary pupils who travel between 1 and 2 miles.

   c Explain what the pie chart tells you.

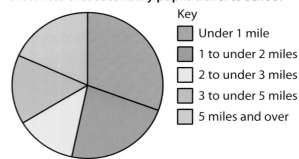

Distances that secondary pupils travel to school

Key
- Under 1 mile
- 1 to under 2 miles
- 2 to under 3 miles
- 3 to under 5 miles
- 5 miles and over

Source: www.dft.gov.uk 1999 – 2001

6 a What is similar about the data in the two pie charts in questions 4 and 5?

   b What is different about the data in the pie charts?

Extension problems

You will need the two bar charts from the extension problems in Exercise 2.

7 The two bar charts show the types of vehicles that use a country road and a main road. For each bar chart, write two sentences to say what the bar chart tells you.

8 What is similar about the two bar charts in question 7? What is different?

⊙ **Points to remember**

- ⊙ **Bar charts** and **pie charts** are ways of displaying data. They help to show **patterns** and **features** in data.
- ⊙ The frequencies of different groups are shown by:
  - – the heights of the bars in a bar chart;
  - – the sizes of the slices in a pie chart.

4 Drawing conclusions and writing a report

This lesson will help you to write a report saying what you found out in your survey.

Exercise 4

A good report includes information about each stage of the data handling cycle.

- **Decide on the problem and plan**
  Write the title and what your survey was about.

- **Collect data**
  Write about how you collected the data.

- **Organise and represent data**
  Put the graphs and tables of the data here.

- **Interpret and discuss data**
  Write about what the graphs show.
  Write a conclusion saying what you found out.

1 Write a title for your report.

Now write at least one full sentence to answer each question.

2 How did you collect your data?
  What did you do?
  Where did you get the data from?
  How many vehicles did you collect data from?
  What data did you collect?

3 How did you record your data?
  Put a copy of this in your report.

4 How did you present your data?
  Put a copy of this in your report.

5 What does your data show?
  For each graph, write down what it shows.

6 Write a conclusion.
  Write a sentence to say what you found out overall.

Points to remember

⊙ Your **conclusion** should be an answer to the original question.

⊙ In your **report**:
  – say what the report is about;
  – explain how you collected the data;
  – include your tables and graphs;
  – write about what the graphs tell you;
  – give your conclusion.

5 Line graphs

This lesson will help you to draw line graphs.

Exercise 5

A holiday company sends out brochures each month.

This **line graph** shows how many brochures were sent out over one year.

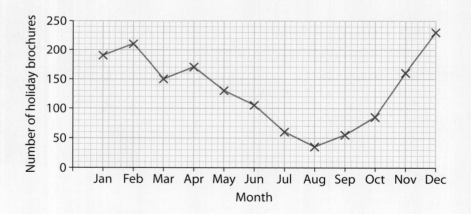

Notice that there are labels on the axes.

The grid lines are labelled, not the spaces.

Points are plotted and joined in order with straight lines, using a ruler.

Example

This table shows how many pennies you get for different numbers of 2p coins.

Number of 2p coins	1	2	3	4	5	6	7	8	9	10
Number of pennies	2	4	6	8	10	12	14	16	18	20

Draw a line graph to show the data in the table.

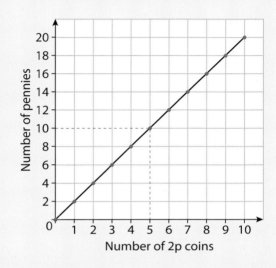

You can see from the graph that when you have five 2p coins you can get ten 1p coins.

You will need squared paper, a ruler and a sharp pencil for these questions.

1. Faisal has some pound coins.
   He wants to change them for 20p coins.

   a How many 20p coins will he get for £2?

   b How many 20p coins will he get for £5?

   c Copy and complete this table.

Number of £1 coins	1	2	3	4	5	6	7	8	9	10
Number of 20p coins										

2 a Draw some axes like this.
Draw a line graph to show the data in the table in question 2.

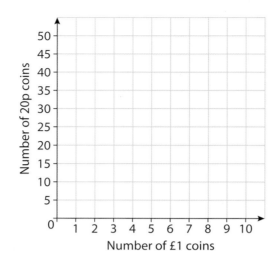

Join your points with a dotted line.

b How many 20p coins will Faisal get for £12?

3 Alma has some 20p coins. She wants to change them for 5p coins.

Copy and complete this table.

Number of 20p coins	1	2	3	4	5	6	7	8	9	10
Number of 5p coins										

4 **a** Draw a line graph to show the data in the table in question 3.

The horizontal axis is for 20p coins. Number it in ones from 0 to 10.
The vertical axis is for 5p coins. Number it in twos from 0 to 40.

Join the points of your graph with a dotted line.

b Estimate how many 5p coins Alma will get for £1.80.

5 Paul is going to Argentina. He will stay in the most southerly city in the world.

He needs to change some British pounds into Argentine pesos.
He gets 6 pesos for £1.

a How many pesos will he get for £2?

b How many pesos will he get for £5?

c Copy and complete this table.

British pounds	1	2	3	4	5	6	7	8	9	10
Argentine pesos										

d Draw a line graph to convert British pounds to Argentine pesos.

Use the horizontal axis for pounds. Number it in ones from 0 to 10.
The vertical axis is for pesos. Number it in fours from 0 to 60.

Join the points on your graph with a solid line.

e Use your graph to work out how many pesos Paul gets for £5.50.

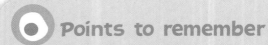
⊙ A **line graph** has points joined in order.

⊙ Label the axes.

⊙ Number the lines, not the spaces, on the axes.

⊙ If the in-between points make sense, join the points with a solid line. If not, join the points with a dotted line.

⊙ Use the graph to read off values and look for patterns.

6 More line graphs

This lesson will help you to learn how to draw and interpret line graphs.

Exercise 6

This **line graph** shows the monthly rainfall in Edinburgh last year.

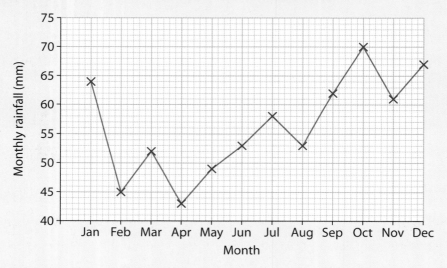

From the line graph, you can tell that:

⊙ The rainfall was highest in October.

⊙ The rainfall was lowest in April.

⊙ There were 53 millimetres of rainfall in each of June and August.

⊙ In general, it was wetter in the winter months.

Line graphs can help you to interpret data. Look for:

⊙ the highest and lowest points;

⊙ where the line goes up so values are increasing;

⊙ where the line goes down so values are decreasing;

⊙ any unusual features.

The source of the data in this exercise is www.weatherbase.com

You will need squared paper, a sharp pencil and a ruler.

1　Monterrey is in Mexico.

The table shows the average temperature in Monterrey for each month of the year.

Month	Jan	Feb	Mar	Apr	May	Jun	Jul	Aug	Sep	Oct	Nov	Dec
Temperature (°C)	14	16	21	24	26	28	28	29	26	23	18	15

a　Draw a line graph to show how the temperature changes over a year.
Put the months on the horizontal axis.
Put degrees (°C) on the vertical axis. Number it in twos from 10 to 30.
Join the points on your graph with a dashed line.

b　In which month is it warmest in Monterrey?

c　In which month is it coldest?

d　Write some sentences describing the temperature in Monterrey.

2 Wellington is in New Zealand.

The table below shows the average temperature in Wellington for each month of the year.

Month	Jan	Feb	Mar	Apr	May	Jun	Jul	Aug	Sep	Oct	Nov	Dec
Temperature (°C)	17	16	16	13	11	10	8	9	10	11	13	15

a Draw a line graph to show how the temperature changes over a year.

Put the months on the horizontal axis. Put degrees (°C) on the vertical axis. Number it in twos from 0 to 20.

Join the points on your graph with a dashed line.

b In which month is it warmest?

c In which month is it coldest?

d Write some sentences describing the temperature in Wellington.

3 This graph shows the temperature in London on 2 May 2008.

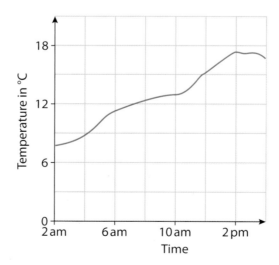

a At what time was the temperature 12 °C?

b At what time was the temperature 15 °C?

c Estimate the temperature at 2:00 pm.

Extension problem

4 The two graphs show the temperature in two different cities.
Look carefully at the axes. They are different.

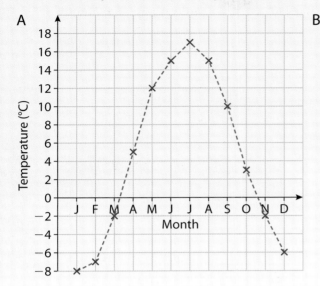

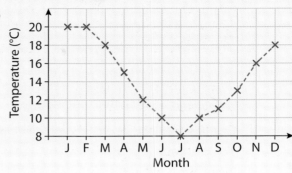

a Write three things describing the temperature in each city.

b Which city has the hottest temperature?

c Which city has the coldest temperature?

d The two cities are Melbourne (Australia) and Moscow (Russia).
Which is which? Explain how you know.

 Points to remember

- Line graphs help to show patterns in data.
- Pick out features such as:
  - the highest point and the lowest point;
  - where the graph is going up and where it is going down;
  - any unusual features such as peaks or dips.

How well are you doing?

Can you:

- interpret tables, charts and graphs?
- look for and describe patterns in data?
- draw simple conclusions and solve problems?

1 *2005 level 4*

A survey showed these results about the number of mobile phones used in the UK.

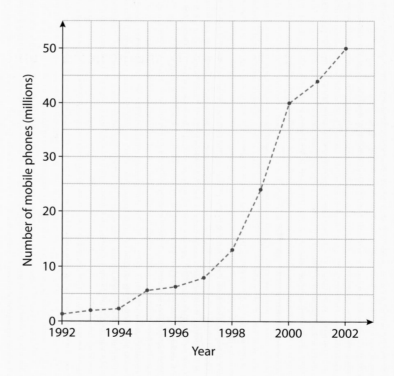

Use the graph to answer the questions.

a Approximately how many millions of mobile phones were there in 1992?

b Approximately how many millions of mobile phones were there ten years later?

c From 1998 to 1999, the number of mobile phones increased by about how many million?

2 *2004 KS2 level 4*

A school has a quiz each year.

There are two teams. Here are their results.

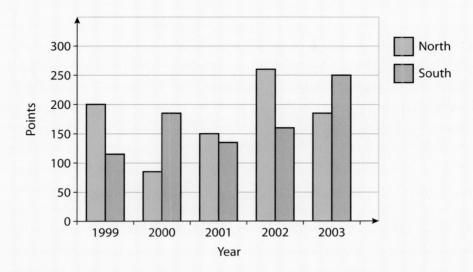

a In which year did North beat South by 100 points?

b In which year did South beat North by the greatest amount?

3 *2000 KS2 level 4*

This bar chart shows how many people went to a school play.

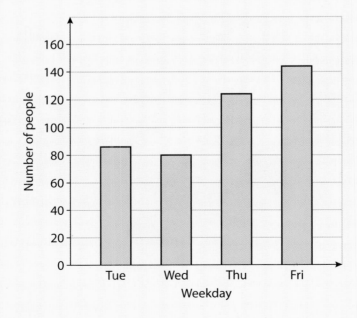

Estimate the number of people who went there on Thursday and Friday altogether.

Solving number problems

This unit will help you to:

- ⊙ use and apply mathematics to help to solve problems;
- ⊙ remember and use number facts;
- ⊙ calculate with whole numbers, decimals and fractions.

---

1 Solving problems with whole numbers

This lesson will help you to solve problems by calculating mentally with whole numbers.

 Did you know that...?

Our word *calculate* comes from the Latin word *calculus*, which means 'pebble'.

Can you see the connections between calculations and pebbles?

The word *thrice*, like the Latin *ter*, means 'three times'.

There are links with the French words *très*, 'very', and *trois*, 'three'.

Some tribal languages have number words but no word for *number*.
Others have words for different colours but no word for *colour*.

Exercise 1

Work with a partner to solve these puzzles.

1 Who am I?

a I am less than 20.
   If you divide me by 4, the reminder is 3.
   If you divide me by 5, the remainder is 4.

b I am an odd multiple of 9.
   The product of my two digits is also a multiple of 9.

c I am a square number.
   The sum of my two digits is one of my factors.

d I am a two-digit number.
   I am not a multiple of 10.
   I am 2 more than a multiple of 9, and 1 less than a multiple of 7.

e I am a three-digit number less than 200.
   If you divide me by 9, the reminder is 3.
   If you divide me by 7, the remainder is 4.

f I am a square number.
   The sum of my two digits is my square root.

2 This is a multiplication table.

Each number is the product of the number at the beginning of the row and the number at the top of the column.

For example, 10 is the product of 2 × 5.
28 is the product of 4 × 7.

×	2	3	4
5	10	15	20
6	12	18	24
7	14	21	28

Copy and complete this multiplication table.

×	5		9	
		8	18	
3				
	35			14
				2

Extension problem

 3 Each ● is where a red ink blot has splashed on a digit.
In each calculation, the three missing digits are 1, 2 and 3.
Copy and complete the calculations.

a ●● × ● = 36

b ●● − ● = 11

c ●● + ● = 33

d ●● ÷ ● = 7

e ●● − ● = 18

f ●● ÷ ● = 4

g ●● × ● = 62

h ●● + ● = 24

● Points to remember

When you are solving problems:

⊙ be systematic;

⊙ look for and make use of patterns;

⊙ keep a careful record of your findings as you go along;

⊙ explain and justify your answers.

2 Solving problems with number sequences

This lesson will help you to recognise and extend sequences.

Exercise 2

A **sequence** is a pattern of numbers that follow a rule.

Here is a sequence made from patterns of crosses.

```
 ✕        ✕ ✕      ✕ ✕ ✕      ✕ ✕ ✕ ✕
 ✕        ✕ ✕      ✕ ✕ ✕      ✕ ✕ ✕ ✕
Pattern 1  Pattern 2  Pattern 3   Pattern 4
```

The **rule** to find the next pattern is 'add a column of 2 crosses'.

The sequence of numbers of crosses is **2, 4, 6, 8**, …

The numbers in the sequence are called **terms** of the sequence.

The 1st term is **2**,
the 2nd term is **4**,
the 3rd term is **6**,
and so on.

The **rule** to find the next term in the sequence is 'add 2'.

Example

Here is a sequence of numbers: 51, 46, 41, …, …, 26, 21

a Write the rule for this sequence.

The difference between each term and the next is 5.

The sequence is going down in steps of 5, so the rule is 'subtract 5'.

b What are the missing terms?

The 4th term is 41 − 5 = 36.

The 5th term is 36 − 5 = 31.

① Copy these sequences. Fill in the missing terms.

a [14] [21] [28] [35] [ ] [ ] [ ]

b [5] [12] [ ] [26] [ ] [40] [ ]

c [80] [72] [64] [56] [ ] [ ] [ ]

d [23] [15] [ ] [−1] [ ] [−17] [ ]

② Write the rule for each sequence and the two missing terms.

a [6] [11] [16] [21] [ ] [ ]

b [1] [2] [4] [8] [ ] [ ]

c [9] [6] [3] [ ] [ ]

d [−11] [−4] [3] [ ] [ ]

③ Here is a sequence. It continues in the same way.

[2] [5] [8] [11] [ ] [ ]

a Write the rule for the sequence.

b Work out the 10th term of the sequence.

4　**a** Madhu has 18 computer games on 3 shelves.
　　 Each shelf has 3 more games than the one above it.
　　 How many games are there on each shelf?

　　b Madhu rearranges the 18 games on the 3 shelves.
　　 Each shelf has 2 less games than the one above it.
　　 How many games are there on each shelf?

　　c Madhu rearranges the 18 games again.
　　 This time she puts them on 4 shelves.
　　 Each shelf has 1 more game that the one above it.
　　 How many games are there on each shelf?

5　The beads in the 3rd, 6th and 9th positions of this sequence are blue.
　　The other beads are red.

　　The sequence continues in the same way.

　　a What position is the next blue bead?

　　b What position is the 6th blue bead?

　　c What colour is the 30th bead? Explain how you know.

　　d What colour is the 301st bead? Explain how you know.

Extension problem

6　Here is a rectangle from the 100-square.
　　The two blue numbers add up to 29.
　　The two green numbers add up to 29.

3	4	5	6
13	14	15	16
23	24	25	26

$3 + 26 = 29$
$23 + 6 = 29$

1	2	3	4	5	6	7	8	9	10
11	12	13	14	15	16	17	18	19	20
21	22	23	24	25	26	27	28	29	30
31	32	33	34	35	36	37	38	39	40
41	42	43	44	45	46	47	48	49	50
51	52	53	54	55	56	57	58	59	60
61	62	63	64	65	66	67	68	69	70
71	72	73	74	75	76	77	78	79	80
81	82	83	84	85	86	87	88	89	90
91	92	93	94	95	96	97	98	99	100

　　a Find some other rectangles with opposite corner numbers that add up to 29.

　　b Find some rectangles with opposite corner numbers that add up to 32.

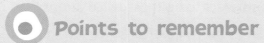
3 Solving problems with decimals

This lesson will help you to solve problems by calculating mentally with decimals.

Exercise 3

Use the facts that you know to work out new facts.

Example 1

Work out 0.6×7.

Work out $6 \times 7 = 42$, then divide by 10.

Answer: 4.2

Example 2

Work out $5.4 \div 6$.

Work out $54 \div 6 = 9$, then divide by 10.

Answer: 0.9

Example 3

Work out 5.4×3.

Split 5.4 into 5 and 0.4.

Multiply each part separately and then add the two parts.

$$5.4 \times 3 = (5 \times 3) + (0.4 \times 3)$$
$$= 15 + 1.2$$
$$= 16.2$$

1 You know that **6 × 7 = 42**. Use this fact to do these calculations.

a 60 × 70　　b 70 × 6　　c 12 × 7　　d 3 × 14　　e 8 × 7

f 6 × 3.5　　g 6 × 14　　h 420 ÷ 6　　i 300 × 7　　j 4.2 ÷ 7

k 12 × 3.5　　l 14 × 12　　m 0.6 × 7　　n 0.42 ÷ 6　　o 1.75 × 6

2 A sports centre has different charges for adults and children.

a Mrs Brown goes swimming every day. How much does she pay each week?

b How much more does it cost for an adult to play squash than to play table tennis?

c Two adults and two children play badminton.
What does it cost them altogether?

d Five children paid for the same sport. Altogether they paid £4.25.
What sport did they pay for?

e Six Year 7 boys went to the gym. How much did they pay altogether?

Sports Centre charges

	Adults	Children
Swimming	£2.50	85p
Badminton	£3.45	£1.60
Gym	£1.65	65p
Table tennis	95p	35p
Squash	£1.78	94p

3 Work these out in your head. Write only the answers.

a 3.7 + 4.5　　b 6.8 − 2.5　　c 4.3 × 4

d 8.8 ÷ 4　　e 9.1 + 4.9　　f 7.0 − 2.7

g 2 × 3.7　　h 2.7 ÷ 9　　i 7.2 + 3.8

j 9.2 − 7.8　　k 5.8 × 9　　l 1.6 ÷ 5

4 Play **Multiplication Bingo** with a partner.

You will need **N2.7 Resource sheet 3.2**, a dice and six counters each.

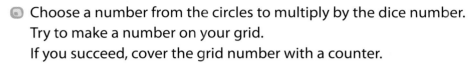

Rules

⊙ Each player uses one of the square grids.

⊙ In turn, roll the dice.

⊙ Choose a number from the circles to multiply by the dice number.
   Try to make a number on your grid.
   If you succeed, cover the grid number with a counter.

⊙ If you can't do it, miss that turn.

⊙ The winner is the first player to cover every number on their grid and call 'Bingo!'

> **Points to remember**
>
> ⊙ Use the facts that you know to work out new facts.
>
> ⊙ To work out a product such as 4.3×6, split the decimal and multiply each part separately.
>
> ⊙ Use jottings to help you if necessary.

4 Solving problems with fractions

This lesson will help you to calculate with simple fractions.

Exercise 4

To add and subtract fractions, change them into fractions with the same denominator.

Example

Work out $\frac{2}{3} + \frac{1}{4}$.

Multiples of 3 are: 3 6 9 **12** 15 …   Multiples of 4 are: 4 8 **12** 16 20 …

The first number that is in both lists is 12.
Change each denominator to 12.

$\frac{2}{3} = \frac{2 \times 4}{3 \times 4} = \frac{8}{12}$ and $\frac{1}{4} = \frac{1 \times 3}{4 \times 3} = \frac{3}{12}$

So $\frac{2}{3} + \frac{1}{4} = \frac{8}{12} + \frac{3}{12} = \frac{11}{12}$

1 Play **Find the fraction** with a partner.
You need two dice.

Rules

- Play with a partner. Take turns.

- In turn, roll the two dice.
  If the two numbers are the same, roll again.

- If they are different, write down a fraction with the smaller number as the numerator
  and the larger as the denominator.

- Roll the two dice again, and write down a second fraction.
  It can be the same or different from the first fraction.

- Add the two fractions to find the total. If you have made a new total, write it down.

- The winner is the first player to make five different totals.

2 Work these out.
Write each answer in its simplest form.

a $\frac{5}{9} - \frac{1}{4}$ b $\frac{5}{6} + \frac{2}{3}$ c $\frac{9}{10} - \frac{3}{4}$ d $\frac{3}{4} + \frac{2}{3} - \frac{5}{6}$

3 a The shops are three fifths of a mile away.
    I have walked one quarter of a mile.
    How far have I still to go?

   b One third of a fruit salad is bananas.
    One quarter is melon.
    What fraction of the fruit salad is other fruits?

   c How much more is one third of a litre than
    one quarter of a litre?

   d A magazine has two adverts on the same page.
    The first advert uses one eighth of the page.
    The second advert uses one fifth of the page.
    What fraction of the whole page do they cover?

4 Choose from these fractions.

$\frac{2}{3}$ $\frac{4}{5}$ $\frac{1}{2}$ $\frac{3}{4}$ $\frac{5}{6}$

Copy and complete these.

a $\bigcirc + \bigcirc = 1\frac{1}{4}$

b $\bigcirc - \bigcirc = \frac{1}{6}$

c $\bigcirc + \bigcirc = 1\frac{7}{15}$

d $\bigcirc - \bigcirc = \frac{1}{3}$

e $\bigcirc + \bigcirc = 1\frac{1}{2}$

f $\bigcirc - \bigcirc = \frac{1}{20}$

5 Work out each of the following.
Write each answer in its simplest form.

a $\frac{7}{8} \times 4$ b $\frac{3}{11} \times 6$ c $12 \times \frac{7}{16}$ d $35 \times \frac{5}{21}$

6 a Nine children each ate three quarters of a pizza.
How many pizzas did they eat altogether?

b Marie fills each of six glasses with two fifths of a litre
of lemonade.
How much lemonade does she use altogether?

c Darren put two thirds of a kilogram of cherries in
each of 12 boxes.
What is the total weight of the cherries in the boxes?

Points to remember

⊙ You can add and subtract fractions only if they have the same
denominator.

⊙ To find a fraction such as $\frac{3}{8}$ of a number, find $\frac{1}{8}$ then multiply by 3.

⊙ Always include any units in the answer.

How well are you doing?

Solving problems (no calculator)

1 *2004 Progress Test level 4*

Copy this equation and fill in the missing fraction.

$$\frac{3}{4} - \square = \frac{1}{2}$$

2 *2005 level 4*

   a Add together 3.7 and 6.5   **b** Subtract 5.7 from 15.2

   c Multiply 254 by 5   **d** Divide 342 by 6

3 *2004 Progress Test level 4*

I am thinking of two numbers.
When I add my numbers, the answer is 11.
When I multiply my numbers, the answer is 24.
What are my numbers?

4 *2006 level 4*

   a These rules show how to get from one number to the next in these sequences.
Use the rules to copy and complete each sequence.

      i Rule: Add 8
Sequence: 4   12   ...   ...

     ii Rule: Multiply by 3
Sequence: 4   12   ...   ...

   b A sequence of numbers starts like this:

      30   22   18

   Could the rule be 'subtract 8'?
Write **Yes** or **No**. Explain your answer.

Functional skills 4

Healthy eating

This group activity will help you to:

- model a situation;
- change values to see the effects on answers;
- select the methods and tools to use, including ICT;
- interpret results and draw conclusions.

General information

Your lunch should give you about one third of your daily requirements.

Here are some of the recommendations.

Girls: at least		Boys: at least	
720 KCal	energy	960 KCal	energy
14 g	protein	24 g	protein
5 mg	iron	5 mg	iron
12 mg	vitamin C	10 mg	vitamin C

Background information

Lunch menu	Price (p)	Energy (KCal)	Protein (g)	Iron (mg)	Vitamin C (mg)
Curried beef and rice	105	290	26	3	2
Egg salad	95	110	8	2	30
Veggie burger	60	45	2	1	5
Sausage (1)	36	180	5	1	0
Spaghetti bolognaise	75	282	25	1	5
Mashed potatoes	18	180	2	0	6
Chips	42	280	5	2	18
Carrots	18	35	1	1	0
Baked beans	36	140	9	3	5
Mixed salad	24	20	0	1	6
Peas	20	60	6	2	1
Orange	30	45	0	1	178
Banana	30	65	0	0	6
Trifle	36	160	3	1	2
Yogurt	24	70	5	0	0
Jam sponge	45	250	3	1	0
Custard	15	90	3	0	0

Problem

Creating a balanced meal

Create some different meals which meet the recommendations.

Try to create some that would suit different tastes.
For example, include a meal for a vegetarian, and for someone who is allergic to milk.

Set out your suggestions systematically.

What is the cheapest meal that you can find that fulfils the recommendations?

Join with another pair to discuss your meals.

Now design a poster to display your joint recommendations.

Revision unit 1

This unit will help you to:

- revise the work you have done so far during the year;
- answer test questions.

Many of the questions are from National Curriculum test papers (SATs).

1 Measures and measuring scales

This lesson will remind you how to estimate, measure and use measuring scales.

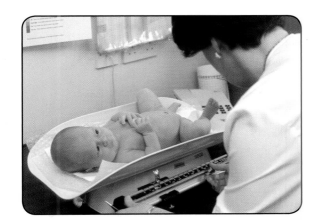

Exercise 1

You need to know these relationships.

Length		Weight
10 mm = 1 cm		1000 g = 1 kg
100 cm = 1 m		
1000 mm = 1 m		**Capacity/volume**
1000 m = 1 km		1000 ml = 1 litre

This diagram can help you to convert between units of length.

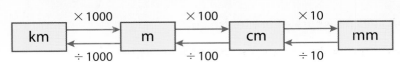

Answer questions 1 to 6 **without using your calculator**.

1 *Mental Test questions level 4*

    a How many millimetres are there in 15 centimetres?

    b How many metres are there in 4.5 kilometres?

    c How many millilitres are there in three quarters of a litre?

    d The perimeter of a regular octagon is 40 centimetres.
       What is the length of each side?

2 *2003 Progress Test level 3*

Which value completes each sentence?

    a The length of a banana is about …

      2 cm   20 cm   200 cm   2000 cm

    b The weight of an apple is about …

      1 gram   10 grams   100 grams   1000 grams

3 *2006 KS2 level 3*

Here is a baby's drinking cup.

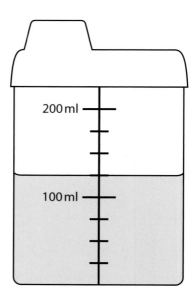

How many millilitres of water are in the cup?

(4) *2005 Progress Test level 4*

a The diagram shows Jo's key.
Use the scale to find the length
of Jo's key.

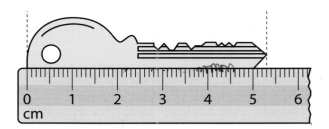

b This time you cannot see all of Jo's key.
One end is at 2.8 cm on the scale.
Where is the other end on the scale?

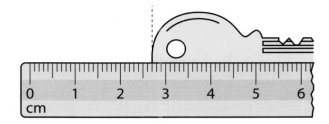

For questions 5 to 11 you may **use a calculator** if you wish.

(5) *2003 KS2 level 3*

Emily is making a cake.
She puts flour on the scales.
She then adds sugar to the flour.

How much sugar does she add?
Show your working.

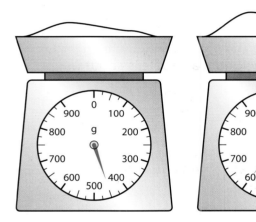

(6) *2004 KS2 level 4*

a This scale shows the weight of Fred's cat.

What is the weight of Fred's cat?

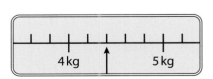

b This scale shows the weight of Fred's dog.

How much more does Fred's dog weigh
than his cat?

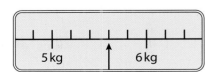

(7) *2006 KS2 level 4*

Lin has five blocks which are all the same.
She balances them on the scale with two weights.

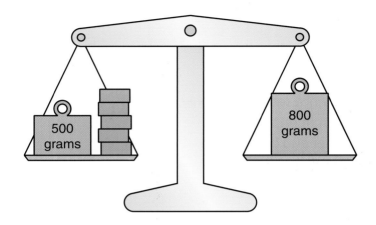

Calculate the weight of one block. You may **use your calculator**.

(8) *2004 Progress Test level 3*

The chart shows the distances in miles between five cities in America.

	Chicago			
Denver	1015	Denver		
New York	797	1799	New York	
Seattle	2062	1329	2864	Seattle
Washington	701	1686	228	2769

Use the chart to answer these questions.

a   It is 1686 miles from Washington to Denver.
   How many miles is it from Washington to Chicago?

b   Which two cities have the greatest distance between them?

c   To change miles to kilometres use this rule:

miles ⟶ × 1.6 ⟶ kilometres

How many kilometres is it from New York to Washington?
You may **use your calculator**.

9 *2003 KS2 level 4*

A bottle holds 1 litre of fruit drink.

Rachel fills 5 glasses with fruit drink.

She puts 150 millilitres in each glass.

How much fruit drink is left in the bottle?
Show your working.

Extension problem

10 *2006 level 5*

Copy and complete these sentences.

a   120 mm is the same as … cm.   b   120 mm is the same as … m.

c   120 m is the same as … km.

⊙ **Points to remember**

- ⊙ **Kilo** means 1000, **centi** means one hundredth and **milli** means one thousandth.
- ⊙ To read a scale:
    - – decide what each interval represents;
    - – work out the numbers for the marks near the pointer;
    - – if the pointer lies between marks, estimate the reading.
- ⊙ If an answer is a measurement, remember to include the units.

---

2 Solving number problems

This lesson will remind you how to solve number and money problems.

There are many different puzzles and problems to solve based on money.

1 *2006 level 3*

A shop sells three different-sized bottles of lemonade.

a I want 3 litres of lemonade.
I could buy three bottles of size 1 litre.
How much would that cost?

b Write a different way I could buy exactly 3 litres of lemonade.
Now work out how much it would cost.

c Write another different way I could buy exactly 3 litres of lemonade.
Now work out how much it would cost.

d My friend buys seven bottles of lemonade.
Two of the bottles are of size $1\frac{1}{2}$ litres.
Five of the bottles are of size 2 litres.
How many litres is that altogether?

39p   55p   70p

2 *2003 Progress Test level 3*

The pictures show all the different euro banknotes.

a Marco has four banknotes.
Altogether he has eight hundred euros.
What banknotes could Marco have?
Write the value of each of the banknotes.

b Anna also has four banknotes that total eight hundred euros.
Her banknotes are not exactly the same as Marco's.
What banknotes could Anna have?

3 *2003 level 3*

Look at these prices.

a Copy these sentences.
Use the prices to complete them.

The total cost of two rulers and one pencil is ......

The total cost of three blue pens is ....

55p is the total cost of one blue pen and ....

Ruler	30p
Pencil	15p
Blue pen	35p
Green pen	40p
Eraser	20p

b There are many different ways to make the total cost of the items 60p.
Write four different ways to do it.

4 *2004 level 4*

There are seven different ways to make 8p with coins.

Copy and complete the table to show the seven ways to make 8p.

Two have been done for you.

Number of 5p coins	Number of 2p coins	Number of 1p coins
0	0	8
0	1	6

5 *2004 Progress Test level 4*

The card shows the price of dinner at a restaurant.

a Twelve people had dinner.
How much did they pay altogether?

b Another restaurant has different prices.
Two adults and their children had dinner.
They paid £58.05 altogether.
How many children had dinner?

> **Dinner**
> **£14.95 each**

> **Dinner**
> **adults £14.95 each**
> **children half price**

6 *2004 level 4*

I buy a widescreen television costing £1290.
I pay £900 now, then I pay the rest of the money in 3 equal payments.
How much is each payment?
Show your working.

Extension problem

 2003 level 5

A car park shows this sign.

> # Car Parking
> ## 70p
> Pay using any of these coins:
>
> 10p 20p 50p
>
> ---
> No change given

Copy and complete the table to show all the different ways of paying exactly 70p.

Number of 10p coins	Number of 20p coins	Number of 50p coins
7	0	0

⊙ Points to remember

When you solve number problems, remember to:

- ⊙ be systematic;
- ⊙ record your findings as you go along;
- ⊙ look for patterns;
- ⊙ use them to draw conclusions;
- ⊙ explain what you have found out.

3 Sequences and patterns

This lesson will remind you how to describe and generate simple sequences, identify factors of numbers, and read and plot coordinates.

Exercise 3

This is a **sequence** of numbers: 5, 10, 15, 20, …
The numbers go up in steps of 5.

The **rule** to find the next term is 'add 5'.
The sequence can be shown on a number line

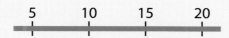

Example

Here is a sequence of shapes made with red and white tiles.

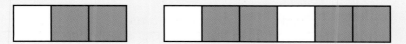

The next shape will have three white tiles and six red tiles.
The number of white tiles is 1 × the shape number.
The number of red tiles is 2 × the shape number.

---

1 *2003 KS2 level 3*

Copy this sequence and fill in the missing numbers.

    64   32   16   …   4   …

2 *1998 KS2 level 3*

Copy this sequence and fill in the missing numbers.

    480   240   …   60   …   15

3 *1999 KS2 level 4*

Halid makes a sequence of five numbers.
The first number is 2.
The last number is 18.
His rule is to add the same amount each time.
Copy and complete his sequence of numbers.

    2   …   …   …   18

4 *1997 level 3*

a Look at this part of a number line.

Copy and complete this sentence:

The numbers on this number line go up in steps of ......

b This is a different number line.
Draw the number line and fill in the three missing numbers.

c This is a different number line.
Draw the number line and fill in the three missing numbers.

d This is a different number line.
Draw the number line and fill in the two missing numbers.

Copy and complete this sentence:

The numbers on this number line go up in steps of ......

e This is a different number line.
Draw the number line and fill in the three missing numbers.

Copy and complete this sentence:

The numbers on this number line go up in steps of ......

5 *2007 level 4*

a A three-digit number is a multiple of 4.
What could the number be? Give an example.
Now give a different example.

b A two-digit number is a factor of 100.
What could the number be? Give an example.
Now give a different example.

Megan wants to plant 24 seeds.
She can plant them like this in 2 rows, with 12 seeds in each row.

. . . .

. . . .

a Draw a diagram to show how she can plant 24 seeds in 3 rows with the same number
of seeds in each row.

b Draw a diagram to show a different way that Megan can plant 24 seeds in a different
number of rows, with the same number of seeds in each row.

c Copy and complete the table to show how many rows Megan can make with 24 seeds,
and how many seeds there are in each row.

Number of rows	Number of seeds in each row
1 row	24 seeds in a row
2 rows	12 seeds in a row
… rows	… seeds in a row
… rows	… seeds in a row
… rows	… seeds in a row
8 rows	3 seeds in a row
12 rows	2 seeds in a row
24 rows	1 seed in a row

d Megan says:

I can plant 24 seeds in 5 rows,
with the same number of seeds
in each row.

Explain why Megan is wrong.
You can write your answer, or draw a diagram.

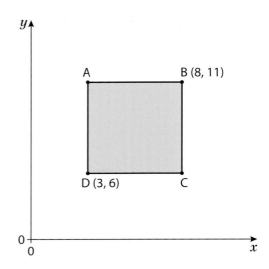

7 *2003 KS2 level 4*

Here is a shaded square.
Write the coordinates of point A.

8 *1996 KS2 level 3*

A, B and C are three corners of a square.
What are the coordinates of the other corner?

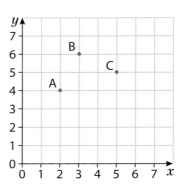

Extension problem

9 *2005 level 5*

a   Is 3 a factor of 30?
    Write **Yes** or **No**. Explain how you know.

b   I am thinking of a number that is greater than 3.
    My number is a factor of 30.
    What could my number be? Give an example.

◉ Points to remember

- A **sequence** of numbers follows a **rule**.
- If a sequence has equal steps, you can work out the rule and the next terms.
- A **factor** of a number divides exactly into the number.
  For example, the factors of 6 are 1, 2, 3 and 6.
- To plot (4, 5) on a grid, start at (0, 0); go 4 steps to the right and 5 up.

4 Perimeter and area

This lesson will remind you how to:

- measure and draw lines to the nearest millimetre;
- measure and calculate perimeters of shapes;
- find areas by counting squares;
- use the formula 'length × width' for the area of a rectangle.

 Did you know that...?

The **tangram** is a Chinese puzzle.
A square is cut into seven pieces, which are rearranged to form pictures and patterns.

Each pattern has the same area because it is made from the same seven pieces.

Exercise 4A

The **perimeter** of a shape is the total distance around the outside of the shape.
You can work out the perimeter of a shape by adding up all the lengths of the sides.

Example 1

Find the perimeter of this shape.

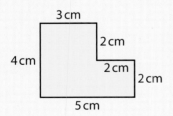

The perimeter is all the way round the edge.
To find the answer, add together the lengths of all the sides:

3 cm + 2 cm + 2 cm + 2 cm + 5 cm + 4 cm
= 18 cm

Example 2

The length of a side of a regular pentagon is 7 cm.

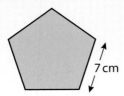

What is the length of its perimeter?

A regular pentagon has 5 equal sides.
Each side is 7 cm long, so the perimeter is:

7 × 5 = 35 cm

1   Use a ruler to measure the lengths of these lines.

    a ▬▬▬▬▬▬   b ▬▬▬▬

    c ▬▬▬▬▬▬▬▬▬▬▬▬

2   Use a ruler to draw lines of these lengths. Label each line with its length.

    a   7 cm   b   59 mm   c   11.2 cm

3   Calculate the perimeter of each of these shapes.

    a 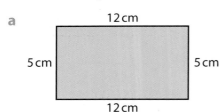   b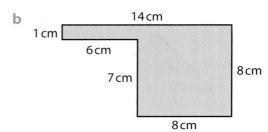

Exercise 4B

Area is a measure of the surface covered by a shape.
You can find the area of a shape by counting the number of squares that it covers.
You can find the area of a rectangle by working out **length × width**.

Example 3

Find the area of this shape.   Count the squares to find the area of the shape.

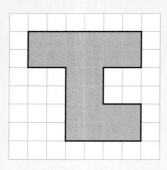   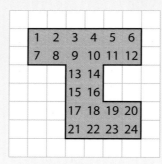

Area = 24 squares

Example 4

Find the area of this rectangle.

Area of a rectangle = length × width

So the area of the rectangle is:

10 cm × 3 cm = 30 cm²

Joe makes different shapes using four tiles each time.
The square grid shows the different shapes he makes.

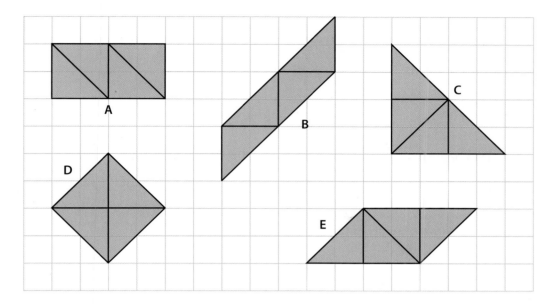

a   Which shape is a square? Write its letter.

b   Which shape is not a quadrilateral? Write its letter.

c   Joe says: 'The shape with the biggest area is shape C.'
    Is Joe correct? Explain your answer.

② 2004 level 4

The diagram shows some shapes on a 10 by 6 square grid.

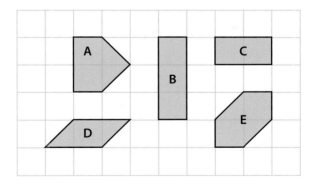

a   Which two shapes have the same area as shape A?

b   Which two shapes have the same perimeter as shape A?

c   How many of shape C would you need to cover a 10 by 6 square grid?

2003 level 4

Look at the hexagon and the triangle.

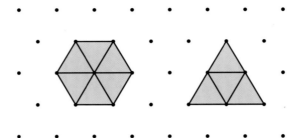

a Do the hexagon and triangle have the same area? Explain your answer.

b Do the hexagon and triangle have the same perimeter? Explain your answer.

4 Calculate the area of each of these rectangles.

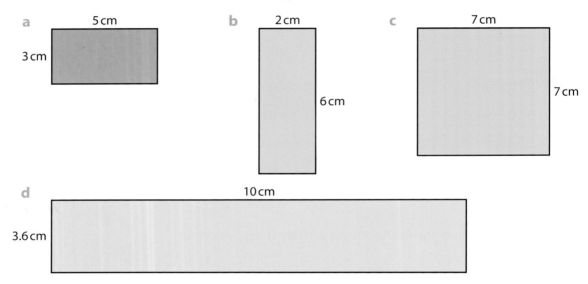

a 5 cm 3 cm

b 2 cm 6 cm

c 7 cm 7 cm

d 10 cm 3.6 cm

Points to remember

- 1 metre = 100 centimetres and 1 centimetre = 10 millimetres.
- Measure lines from 0 on the ruler.
- **Perimeter** is the total distance around the edge of a shape.
  Perimeter is measured in units of length such as mm, cm or mm.
- Calculate the perimeter by adding all the lengths of the sides.
- **Area** is a measure of the surface that a shape covers.
  Area is measured in square units such as mm^2, cm^2, m^2.
- **Area of a rectangle** = length × width.

5 Drawing and interpreting graphs and charts

This lesson will remind you how to represent and interpret data in tables, diagrams, charts and graphs.

Exercise 5

Here are some ways to represent the marks out of 10 that 28 pupils scored in a spelling test.

Tally chart

Score	Tally	Frequency
5	III	3
6	II	2
7	IIII I	6
8	IIII III	8
9	IIII II	7
10	II	2

Bar chart

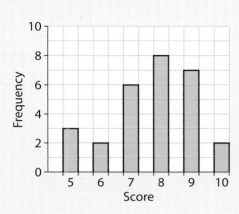

Bar-line graph

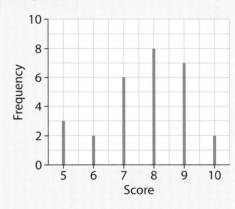

Pie chart

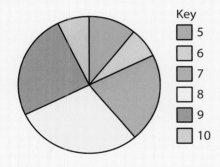

Key
- 5
- 6
- 7
- 8
- 9
- 10

1. *2004 Progress Test level 4*

   The graph shows how the price of a chocolate bar has changed.

   Copy and complete these sentences.

   a Between 1992 and 2002, the price of the chocolate bar increased by …p.

   b In 1992, the price of the chocolate bar was 6 times as much as in …

   c The smallest increase in price was in the five years between … and …

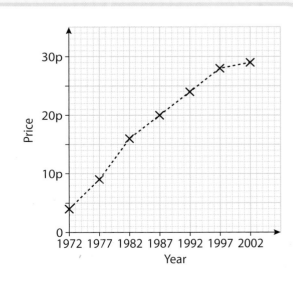

(2) *1997 KS2 level 4*

Gavin was ill in March. This is his temperature chart.

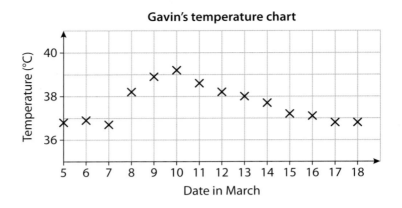

Gavin's temperature chart

a   For how many days was his temperature marked as more than 37 °C?

b   Which date showed the largest change in temperature from the day before?

c   Estimate Gavin's highest temperature shown on the graph.
    Give your answer to one decimal place.

(3) *2000 KS2 level 4*

A camping shop sells tents, sleeping bags and backpacks.
This chart shows how many of each they sold in June.

Items sold in June

Tents	⛺ 🛖
Sleeping bags	▦ ▦ ▦ ⊟
Backpacks	⊠ ⊠ ⊠ ⊠ ⊠ ⊠ △

Key: ⛺ is **4** tents   ▦ is **4** sleeping bags   ⊠ is **4** backpacks

a   The shop had 20 sleeping bags at the beginning of June.
    How many of these sleeping bags did the shop have left at the end of June?

b   In July, the shop sold three times as many tents as in June.
    How many tents did the shop sell in July?

Li and Sue do the same survey.
Their pictograms represent the same information.

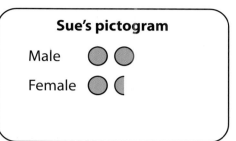

Li's pictogram

Male ☐ ☐ ☐ ☐

Female ☐ ☐ ☐ ☐

Key: ☐ represents 2 people

Sue's pictogram

Male ● ●

Female ● ◖

Sue has forgotten to write her key.
How many people does ● represent?

5 *1998 level 4*

Jim, Bob, Liz and Meg had a games competition.
They played two games, Draughts and Ludo.
Each pupil played each of the others at the two games.

Meg recorded how many
games each person won.

Jim	|||
Meg	|||
Liz	||||
Bob	||

Jim recorded who won
each game.

Draughts	Ludo
Jim	Meg
Liz	Bob
Bob	
Jim	Meg
Jim	Liz
Liz	Meg

a Jim forgot to put one of the names on his table.
   Use Meg's table to work out what the missing name is.

b Who won the most games of Draughts?

c Give one reason why Meg's table is a good way of recording the results.

d Give one reason why Jim's table is a good way of recording the results.

6 Elmer and Kate each throw a dice 20 times.
   The bar-line graphs show their results.

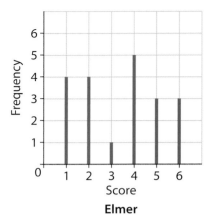

Elmer

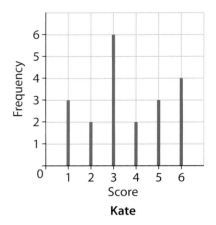

Kate

a What was Elmer's most common score?

b What was Kate's most common score?

c What was Elmer's least common score?

d What was Kate's least common score?

e How many more times did Kate get a score of 3 compared to Elmer?

7 *2006 Mental Test level 4*

In a quiz, pupils were asked a question.
The pictogram shows how many pupils were
right and how many were wrong.

Eight pupils were right.
How many pupils were wrong?

| Right | ● ● ● ● |
| Wrong | ● ◖ |

8 *2006 Mental Test level 4*

A teacher asked some pupils which flavour
drink they preferred.
The bar chart shows the results.

Twenty pupils said orange.
About how many said lime?

| | Lime |
| Orange | |
0   20

⊙ Points to remember

⊙ Graphs, charts and tables are useful for displaying data and making the
   data easier to interpret.

⊙ Read the scale of a graph carefully.

⊙ Use the key for a pictogram to work out how many each symbol represents.

⊙ Read questions carefully so that you know what you need to find out.

Revision unit 2

This unit will help you to:

- revise the work you have done so far during the year;
- answer test questions.

Many of the questions are from National Curriculum test papers (SATs).

1 Inverse operations

This lesson will remind you how to solve problems involving inverse operations.

Exercise 1

To solve 'missing-number' problems, you can use the opposite or **inverse operation**.

- The inverse of $+$ is $-$.
- The inverse of $\times$ is $\div$.
- The inverse of $-$ is $+$.
- The inverse of $\div$ is $\times$.

Example 1

$19 + \square = 32$
What number goes in the box?

The inverse of $+$ is $-$.
Calculate $32 - 19 = 13$.
The number 13 goes in the box.

To **check an answer**, you can use the opposite or **inverse operation**.

Example 2

A pupil thinks that 16×35 is 560.
Check his answer.

The inverse of $\times$ is $\div$.
Calculate $560 \div 35 = 16$.
The answer is 16 so the pupil was right.

Answer questions 1–6 **without using your calculator**.

1. *2003 Progress Test level 3*

   Copy and complete these calculations. Fill in the missing numbers.

   a $36 + \ldots = 100$

   b $100 - \ldots = 51$

   c $\ldots \times 5 = 100$

   d $100 \div \ldots = 25$

2 *2002 KS2 level 3*

What is the missing number in each of these calculations?

a $\square \times 5 = 350$

b $4 \times \square = 200$

3 *2004 Progress Test level 3*

a The numbers on these cards should have a total of 50.
What is the missing number?

| 14 | 12 | |

b The numbers on these cards should have a total of 50.
What could the missing numbers be?

| | 16 | |

4 *2001 level 3*

Look at this multiplication table.

×	11	12	13	14	15
21	231	252	273	294	315
22	242	264	286	308	330
23	253	276	299	322	345
24	264	288	312	336	360
25	275	300	325	350	375

Use the table to copy and complete these calculations.

a $24 \times 13 = \ldots$

b $15 \times \ldots = 300$

c $288 \div 24 = \ldots$

d $\ldots \times \ldots = 264$

5 *2005 Progress Test level 4*

a This pair of decimal numbers adds to 1.

$0.3 + 0.7 = 1$

Write a different pair of decimal numbers that adds to 1.

b The pair of decimal numbers below should add to 1.
Write the missing decimal number.

$0.85 + \square = 1$

2004 KS2 level 4

What are the missing numbers A, B, C and D
in this multiplication grid?

×	5	A	B
4	20	36	32
C	35	63	56
D	30	54	48

For questions 7 – 10 you may **use your calculator**.

7　*2006 level 4*

Copy and complete these calculations. Fill in the missing numbers.

a　$4 \times \ldots + 20 = 180$　　b　$4 \times 20 + \ldots = 180$　　c　$4 \times \ldots - 20 = 180$

8　*2001 level 4*

Copy and complete these calculations. Fill in the missing numbers.

a　$\square \div 13.5 = 50$　　b　$180 + \square = 2700$　　c　$180 \times \square = 2700$

Extension problems

9　I'm thinking of a number.
I work out the product of 8 and my number.
The answer is 320.
What is my number?

10　The table shows part of a multiplication grid.
Copy the table.
Fill in the missing numbers.

×			6
2	10	14	12
	30		36
	35	49	42

Points to remember

⊙ Addition and subtraction are **inverse operations**.

⊙ Multiplication and division are **inverse operations**.

⊙ Use inverse operations to find missing numbers in calculations like:

$18 \times \square = 270$

⊙ Use inverse operations to check answers to calculations.

2 Equivalent fractions, decimals and percentages

This lesson will remind you how to use equivalent fractions, decimals and percentages.

Exercise 2

35 per cent means 35 out of 100.

This is $\frac{35}{100}$ as a fraction and 0.35 as a decimal.

Learn these percentage, fraction and decimal equivalents.

Percentage	100%	50%	25%	75%	10%	20%	1%
Fraction	$\frac{100}{100} = 1$	$\frac{50}{100} = \frac{1}{2}$	$\frac{25}{100} = \frac{1}{4}$	$\frac{75}{100} = \frac{3}{4}$	$\frac{10}{100} = \frac{1}{10}$	$\frac{20}{100} = \frac{1}{5}$	$\frac{1}{100}$
Decimal	1	0.5	0.25	0.75	0.1	0.2	0.01

① *2006 KS2 level 4*

Choose from these fractions.

$\frac{3}{4}$ $\frac{2}{10}$ $\frac{1}{4}$ $\frac{2}{5}$

a Which fraction is equivalent to 0.25?

b Which fraction is equivalent to 0.4?

c Which fraction is equivalent to 0.75?

d Which fraction is equivalent to 0.2?

② *1998 KS2 level 4*

a Which of these cards shows more than a half?

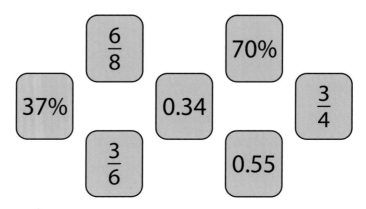

b Which two cards are equivalent?

3 Write each percentage as a decimal.

a 53%　　　　　b 85%　　　　　c 20%　　　　　d 4%

4 Write each decimal as a percentage.

a 0.71　　　　　b 0.35　　　　　c 0.7　　　　　d 0.3

5 *1996 level 4*

Simon is growing vegetables in three vegetable patches.

a About 50% of this vegetable patch is for carrots.

Copy and complete these sentences.
Fill in each gap with a percentage.

About …% of the patch is for cabbages.

About …% of the patch is for lettuces.

| carrots | cabbages |
| | lettuces |

b About $\frac{1}{8}$ of this vegetable patch is for beetroot.

Copy and complete these sentences.
Fill in each gap with a fraction.

About … of the patch is for broad beans.

About … of the patch is for peas.

| beetroot |
| broad beans |
| peas |

c Draw another patch like this.

About $\frac{4}{5}$ of this patch is for potatoes.
Draw a straight line to show how much of this patch is for potatoes.
Shade in the area for potatoes.

The rest of this patch is for leeks.
About what percentage of the patch is for leeks?

(6) Write each percentage as a fraction in its simplest form.

a 90%   b 25%   c 60%   d 5%

(7) *1995 level 4*

Some pupils are climbing up the ropes in the gym.
These are their positions after climbing for a few seconds.

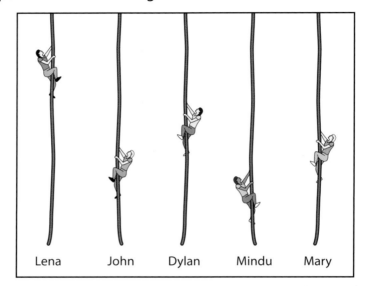

Lena   John   Dylan   Mindu   Mary

a Copy and complete these sentences. Fill each gap with a fraction.

Dylan is about … of the way up the rope.

Lena is about … of the way up the rope.

John is about … of the way up the rope.

b Copy and complete these sentences. Fill each gap with a percentage.

Dylan is about …% of the way up the rope.

Mindu is about …% of the way up the rope.

Mary is about …% of the way up the rope.

c Anna is climbing a longer rope.
She has climbed $\frac{3}{5}$ of the way up the rope.
What percentage of the rope has Anna climbed?

Points to remember

⊙ You can change a fraction to a decimal by dividing the numerator by the denominator. You can use a calculator to do this.

⊙ Equivalent fractions, decimals and percentages are represented by the same point on a number line.

3 Expressions and equations

This lesson will remind you how to substitute numbers into expressions and solve simple equations.

Exercise 3

When there are no brackets do **multiplication and division** before **addition and subtraction**.

For example:

$3 + 4 \times 5 = 23$

You can put in **brackets** to change the **order of operations**. For example:

$(3 + 4) \times 5 = 35$

To solve 'missing-number' problems, you can use **inverse operations**.

- The inverse of $+$ is $-$.
- The inverse of $-$ is $+$.
- The inverse of $\times$ is $\div$.
- The inverse of $\div$ is $\times$.

Example

$16 \times \square = 48$
What number goes in the box?

The inverse of $\times$ is $\div$. Calculate $48 \div 16 = 3$.
The number 3 goes in the box.

---

1 *2004 level 3*

Copy and complete these calculations. Fill in the missing numbers.

   a $3 \times 4 \times \square = 96$ **b** $\square + 62 - 46 = 96$

2 *2003 KS2 level 3*

Copy and complete these calculations. Fill in the missing numbers.

   a $37 \times \square = 111$ **b** $225 - \square = 150$ **c** $\square \div 4 = 21$

3 *2001 KS2 level 3*

Copy and complete these calculations. Fill in the missing numbers.

   a $45 + \square = 110$ **b** $4 \times 5 - \square = 12$ **c** $60 \times 3 = \square$

4 *1999 level 4*

Copy and complete these calculations. Fill in the missing numbers.

   a $400 + 150 = 500 + \square$ **b** $4 + 6 = 4 + \square$ **c** $37 - 20 = 27 - \square$

   d $6 \times 5 = 3 \times \square$ **e** $38 + 17 = 28 + \square$ **f** $38 - 17 = 28 - \square$

   g $40 \times 10 = 4 \times \square$ **h** $7000 \div 100 = 700 \div \square$

5 *1999 KS2 level 3*

Rob has some number cards.

a He holds up a card. He says:

'If I multiply the number on this card by 5, the answer is 35.'

What is the number on the card?

b He holds up a different card. He says:

'If I divide the number on this card by 6, the answer is 4.'

What is the number on the card?

6 *1998 KS2 level 4*

What is the value of $4x + 7$ when $x = 5$?

7 *2005 Mental Test level 4*

Look at this equation.

$$b = 14 + a$$

When $a = 7$, what is the value of b?

8 *2005 Progress Test level 4*

The equation shows how much you pay to hire a car.

N stands for the number of days

$$N \times 20 = T$$

T stands for the total you pay in £

a Leena hires the car for 10 days.
How much must she pay?

b Later, Tom pays £280 to hire the car.
For how many days does he hire the car?

a Look at this equation.

$$x + y = 30$$

What could the values of x and y be? Give one pair of values.

Now give a different pair of values that x and y could be.

b Here is a different equation.

$$a - b = 30$$

When $a = 40$, what is the value of b?

> ### ◉ Points to remember
>
> ⊙ When there are no brackets, do multiplication and division before addition and subtraction.
> ⊙ An **expression** is a combination of numbers and letters, such as $8x - 3$.
> ⊙ You can **substitute** numbers for letters in an expression.
>   For example, when $x = 2, 8x - 3 = 8 \times 2 - 3 = 13$.
> ⊙ Use **inverse operations** to find missing numbers in calculations like:
> $73 + \square = 204$

4 Symmetry and reflection

This lesson will remind you how to draw lines of symmetry on a 2D shape and reflect a shape in a mirror line.

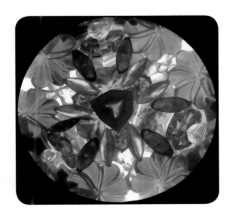

In the picture the bridge is reflected in the water.
So are the trees and houses in the background.

Can you see the line of symmetry?

This Volkswagen car badge has one line of symmetry.
Can you see where it is?

Example 1

How many lines of symmetry are there in this Mercedes car badge?

There are three lines of symmetry in the car badge.

Example 2

How many lines of symmetry are there in a rectangle?

A rectangle has 2 lines of symmetry.

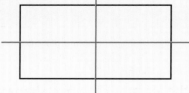

When a shape is reflected in a mirror line, corresponding points are the same distance from the mirror line. This is shown by the green lines.

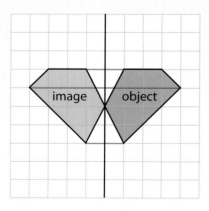

You need copies of **R2.2 Resource sheets 4.1 and 4.2**.

1 Look at these road signs taken from the Highway Code.
How many lines of symmetry are there in each sign?

a Two-way
traffic ahead

b Tunnel
ahead

c Cycle route
ahead

d No stopping
(Clearway)

2 *2004 KS2 level 4*

Here are five shapes on a square grid.

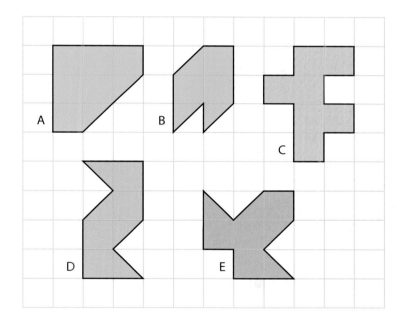

Write the letters of the two shapes which have a line of symmetry.

3 On **Resource sheet 4.1**, reflect each shape in the given mirror line.

a 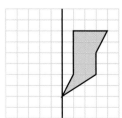 **b** 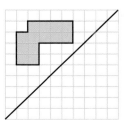 **c** 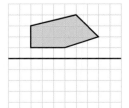 **d**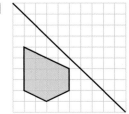

4 *1995 level 4*

On **Resource sheet 4.1**, draw all the lines of symmetry on each design.
The first one has been done for you.

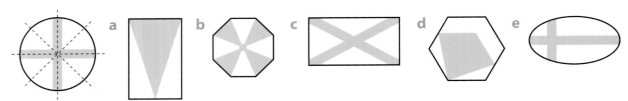

5 *1996 level 4*

On **Resource sheet 4.2**, shade more squares to make symmetrical shapes.

a   Shade one more square.

b   Shade two more squares.

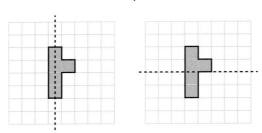

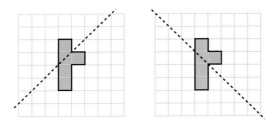

6 *2002 level 4*

a   I have a rectangle made out of paper.
The rectangle measures 12 cm by 8 cm.

I want to fold the rectangle in half to make
a smaller rectangle.
I can do this in two different ways.
What size could the smaller rectangle be?
Give both possibilities.

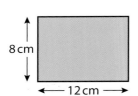

b   I have a square made out of paper.
The square measures 20 cm by 20 cm.
I keep folding it in half until I have a rectangle that is 5 cm by 10 cm.

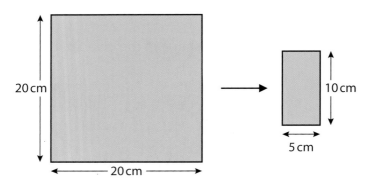

How many times did I fold it?

Points to remember

- A **line of symmetry** or **mirror line** divides a shape into half so that one half folds exactly on top of the other half.
- The starting shape is the **object**.
- The reflected shape is the **image**.
- Matching points on the object and image are the same distance from the mirror line.
- The line joining matching points on the object and image is at right angles to the mirror line.

5 Probability

This lesson will remind you how to describe the likelihood of events and know where to place them on a probability scale marked 0, $\frac{1}{2}$, 1.

Exercise 5

The probability scale

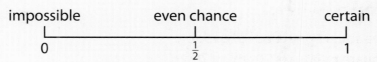

An event that is **impossible** has a probability of 0.

For example, it is impossible that the month after May will be April.

An event that is **certain** has a probability of 1.

For example, it is certain that the sun will rise tomorrow.

An event that has an **even chance** has a probability of $\frac{1}{2}$.

For example, in a pack of playing cards there is an even chance of picking a red card.

Other words that describe the likelihood of events include **likely** and **unlikely**.

For example, it is likely that it will snow in Scotland next year.
I am unlikely to get lost on the way home from school.

① *2005 KS2 level 4*

This spinner is a regular octagon.

Make a sketch of the spinner.
Write 1, 2 or 3 in each section of the spinner so that
1 and 2 are equally likely to come up and
3 is the least likely to come up.

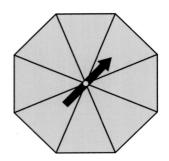

② *2000 KS2 level 4*

The spinner is divided into nine equal sections.

a Which two different numbers on the spinner are
equally likely to come up?

b Meera says:

'2 has a greater than even chance of coming up.'

Explain why she is correct.

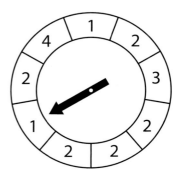

③ The probability scale shows the probabilities for events A, B, C, D, E and F.

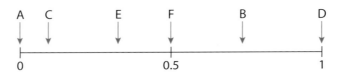

a Which event is impossible?

b Which event is certain?

c Which events are less likely than event E?

d Which event is more likely than F but not certain to happen?

④ *2002 level 4*

I throw a fair coin.
For each statement below, write **True** or **False**, and explain your answer.

a On each throw, the probability of getting a head is $\frac{1}{2}$.

b On four throws, it is certain that I will get two heads and two tails.

5 *1999 KS2 level 4*

Here are two bags.
Each bag has three white balls and one black ball in it.

a A ball is taken from one of the bags without looking.
What is the probability that it is a black ball?
Give your answer as a fraction.

b All the balls from both bags are now mixed together
in a new bag.

Copy the probability scale below. Put a cross (✗) on
the scale to show the probability of taking a black ball
from the new bag.

```
├──────────┼──────────────┼──────────────┼──────────┤
0                                                    1
```

6 *2003 level 4*

A teacher has five number cards.

She says:

'I am going to take a card at random.
Each card shows a different positive whole number.
It is certain that the card will show a number less than 10.
It is impossible that the card will show an even number.'

What numbers are on the cards?

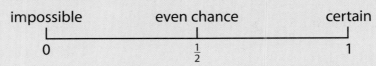

Points to remember

⊙ You can use numbers to describe the likelihood of events:
  – 0 for impossible;
  – 1 for certain;
  – $\frac{1}{2}$ for even chance.

⊙ A **probability scale** can be used to show how likely or unlikely events are.

```
   impossible        even chance       certain
   └──────────────────────┴──────────────────────┘
   0                      1/2                     1
```

Answers to

How well are you doing?

N2.1 Properties of numbers

1. 28 and 35
2. A −19 °C
   B 16 degrees colder
   C −22 °C
3. 25
4. A 4, 16, 36 or 64
   B 1, 9, 25, 49 or 81
   C Any even number that is not a square number
   D Any odd number that is not a square number
5. a 11   b 36
6. a 5 °C   b −9 °C, −3 °C, 0 °C, 6 °C
7. a Any multiple of 10 that does not divide exactly by 20, e.g. 10, 30, 50, 70, 90, 110, …
   b Any multiple of 20 must also be a multiple of 10, so it is not possible to put a number in section B.

S2.1 Graphs, charts and tables

1. a 30   b About 25
   c The fifth bird symbol is not a half square.
2.

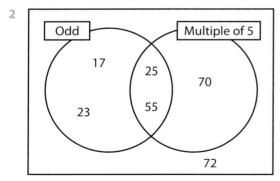

3.

	Multiple of 4	Not a multiple of 4
Two-digit number	12, 24, 20	13, 15, 27, 26, 22, 19
Not a two-digit number	4, 8	6

4. a 6   b 6

N2.2 Whole numbers

1. a 46 + **27** = 73   b 55 − **26** = 29
2. a 257 + 649 = **906**   b 541 − 382 = **159**
3. The newspaper rounded £1758 to the nearest **£100**
4. a 4007   b 3 000 000
5. a 150   b 400
6. 1326 lessons
7. a i 980   ii 375   b 36
8. a 16 × **30** = 480
   b 46 × 22 = **1012**
   c 600 ÷ **12** = 50

A2.1 Patterns and sequences

1. Add 5
2. 2, 8, 14, 20, 26
3. a 105 and 108
   b Yes
4. 4, **7**, **10**, 13, 16, **19**, 22, …
5. a Yes. The sum of the digits is 3 or 3 + 0 = 3.
   b Any one from 5, 6, 10, 15 or 30
6. a Any number between 99 and 1000 where the last two digits are divisible by 4 e.g. 128, 764
   b 10, 20, 25 or 50
7. a 12, 16, 20, 24 etc.
   b 16, 25, 36, 49 etc.

N2.3 Fractions, decimals and percentages

1. a Half
   b More than half
   c Half
2. 0.7 is the same as 7 tenths.
3. a 50%
   b 25%
4. a $\frac{1}{5}$ of 20 = 4
   b $\frac{3}{4}$ of 20 = 15
5. 25%

6   a   5.7   b 6.2

7   a $\frac{2}{12} = \frac{1}{6}$ b $\frac{1}{2} = \frac{12}{24}$ c $\frac{1}{4} = \frac{6}{24}$

8

Sport	Percentage	Number of people
Badminton	10%	26
Football	40%	**104**
Squash	5%	**13**

G2.1 Length, perimeter and area

1   a   The length of a banana is about 20 cm.
    b   The height of the classroom door is about 200 cm.
    c   The width of an exercise book is about 20 cm.

2   a   B and E   b   D and E   c   30

3   a   13 cm   b   1.6 cm or 16 mm

4   a   18 cm^2
    b   Possible dimensions of the rectangle:
       1 cm by 18 cm, 2 cm by 9 cm, 3 cm by 6 cm,
       6 cm by 3 cm, 9 cm by 2 cm, 18 cm by 1 cm

5   280 m^2

6   a   4 mm   b   28 mm

S2.2 Probability 1

1   Any number less than one or greater than eight.

2   A   Impossible   B   Unlikely
    C   Likely   D   Certain

3   A   Least likely   B   Most likely
    C   Impossible

4   a   Box A because there are more yellow counters
       for each blue counter.
    b   Box C contains equal numbers of blue and
       yellow counters.

G2.2 Angles

1   a   Angle a and angle c are the same.
    b   A drawing of an angle greater than 90°
    c   South
    d   South

2   a b b   Yes

3   a   25°   b   115°

4   a   90°   b   30°   c   150°

5   Accurate drawing of 55° angle

6   130°

N2.4 Decimals

1   a   Any number n such that $1000 < n < 1100$
       written in figures
    b   Any decimal number n such that $0 < n < 1$

2   0.74

3   a   £2.86   b   £2.02

4   9.8

5   a   £400   b   £430

6   a   3.5 means £3 and 50 pence.
    b   3.5 means 3 hours and 30 minutes.
    c   3.5 means 3 metres and 50 centimetres.

7   a   3 points
    b   1.5 metres is 150 cm. Sam gets 4 points because
       150 cm is more than 140 cm but less than 160 cm.

A2.2 Sequences, functions and graphs

1   1, 5, 9, 13

2   a   add 12
       multiply by 3
       multiply by 2 then add 6
    b   divide by 2

3

input (x)	1	3	5	10	12
output (y)	10	12	14	19	21

4   a $+3$ b   subtract 5, divide by 2

5

input x →	add 3 →	multiply by 5 →	output y
2		→	25
5		→	40
6		→	45
8		→	55

6   (5, 2)

G2.3 Symmetry and reflection

1   a   C
    b

2

3   These can be in any orientation.

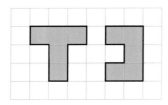

4   4 right, 6 up
    4 left, 6 down

N2.5 Decimals and measures

1   Since 1 litre = 1000 ml, and 500 × 2 = 1000,
    Steve can fill the 500 ml jug twice and pour the
    water into the bucket.

2   a   3.96 m   b   0.2 m

3   a   500 cm   b   90 m   c   8 m

4   750 g ÷ 5 = 150 g

5   Each day, the adult takes 40 ml of medicine and the
    child takes 20 ml, total 60 ml. In 5 days, they take
    60 ml × 5 = 300 ml. There is not enough in the
    250 ml bottle.

6   Claire took 1 hour 25 minutes.
    Tim took 1 hour 20 minutes.
    Claire took 5 minutes longer than Tim.

S2.3 Enquiry 1

1

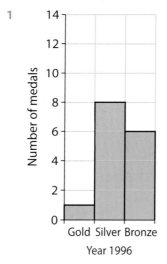

Year 1996

2   a   Monday and Thursday   b   8

3   a   14   b   13

G2.4 Measures

1   25 mm, 3.5 cm, 20 cm, $\frac{1}{2}$ m

2   220 millilitres

3   550 g

4   a   A and D   b   05:15   c   17:15

5   a   10:45 am   b   1:15 pm

6   a   30 minutes   b   9:25

7   2 hours 40 minutes

N2.6 Fractions, percentages and direct proportion

1   a   60 pupils

    b
Number of pupils	Number of teachers
100	5
106	6
197	10

2   a   E

    b   No. $\frac{1}{2}$ of 20 = 10 and $\frac{1}{4}$ of 40 = 10.

3   a $\frac{1}{5}$ of 20 = 4   b $\frac{3}{4}$ of 20 = 15

4   a   4 metres   b   £1.40

5   a   25%   b   5 minutes

6   a   half a lemon, 750 ml water, 450 g of sugar

    b   200 ml

S2.4 Probability 2

1   The game is not fair because there are more odd
    cards than even ones.

2   a   True   b   False   c   False

    Zara is correct, because the biggest number on each
    spinner is 3 so the biggest total you can get is 6.

3   a   On Jill's spinner, 3 is one number out of six, but
        on Peter's it is one number out of eight.

    b   Both spinners have an equal number of odds
        and evens.

G2.5 Properties of shapes

1   Square-based pyramid

2   a   True   b   False

    c   False   d   True

3   a   The shape is a square so the sides must be **all
        the same length**.

    b   The shape is a square so the angles must be
        right angles.

4   Pupils drawings of a trapezium

A2.3 Expressions and equations

1. $4 + 2 = 2 + 4$ ✓
   $4 - 2 = 2 - 4$ ✗
   $4 \times 2 = 2 \times 4$ ✓
   $4 \div 2 = 2 \div 4$ ✗

2. a 18
   b 10
   c 60
   d $(4 + 5 + 1) \times 5 = 50$
   e $4 + (5 + 1) \times 5 = 34$

3. a $36 + \mathbf{64} = 100$ b $100 - \mathbf{49} = 51$
   c $\mathbf{20} \times 5 = 100$ d $100 \div \mathbf{4} = 25$

4. $m = 10$

5. For example:
   a $a = 2, b = 6$
   b $a = 1, b = 5$

6. a £200   b 14

S2.5 Enquiry 2

1. a A number between 1 and 2
   b A number between 49.5 and 50.5
   c A number between 10 and 12

2. a 2002
   b 2000

3. A number between 265 and 280

N2.7 Solving number problems

1. $\frac{3}{4} - \frac{1}{4} = \frac{1}{2}$

2. a 10.2   b 9.5
   c 1270   d 57

3. 3 and 8

4. a i 20, 28   ii 36, 108
   b No. The rule cannot be 'subtract 8' because the difference between the second number and third number is 4, not 8.

Index